SCHOOLS COUNCIL
MODULAR COURSES IN TECH

PNEUMATICS

Peter Patient

Roy Pickup

Norman Powell

Oliver & Boyd

in association with the National Centre for School Technology

PROJECT TEAM

Director
Dr Ray Page

Co-ordinators
Roy Pickup
John Poole

Jeffrey Hall
Dr Duncan Harris
John Hucker
Michael Ive
Peter Patient

Oliver & Boyd
Robert Stevenson House
1-3 Baxter's Place
Leith Walk
Edinburgh EH1 3BB

A Division of Longman Group Ltd

ISBN 0 5 003535 5

First published 1983
Second impression 1984

Printed in Hong Kong
by Hing Yip Printing Co

Contents

Acknowledgments

For permission to reproduce certain photographs and diagrams in this book, the authors and publishers would like to thank the following:

Martonair Limited (Figs. 1.3, 1.4, 1.5, 1.6, 1.9, 2.4, 2.5, 2.7, 2.8, 2.9, 2.10, 2.11, 2.16, 2.18, 3.7, 3.8, 3.9, 4.1, 6.1, 6.11a and 7.16);

Schrader Bellows (Figs. 1.15a, 1.20a and b, 1.23a, 2.14, 3.10, 5.1 and 5.11);

Economatics Limited (Fig. 5.18);

IMI Norgren Limited (Figs. 10.1, 10.5a, 10.6a, 10.10a, 10.16a, 10.18a, 10.23a and 11.27a).

Note   The sign ■ has been used in the text to signify material suitable for both O-level and CSE candidates. The sign □ indicates material required only for the O-level examination.

1 Introduction to Pneumatics

■ Pneumatic Systems

Compressed air is air which has been taken from the atmosphere we breathe and forced into a small space. We compress air every time we blow up a balloon or pump up a bicycle tyre. It is not easy to blow up a lot of balloons or pump up a lot of tyres. In fact, it is quite hard **work** and it takes a lot of muscular **energy**.

Once the air has been compressed in a balloon or tyre, it tries to get out again. It can only do this because it is storing most of the energy used to force it into the small space in the first place. Let go the neck of the balloon and the energy stored in the air inside will make the balloon twirl around the room. This stored energy is doing work in moving the balloon like this.

Any system which uses the energy stored in compressed air to do useful work is called a **pneumatic system**. (The word 'pneumatic' comes from the Greek word for 'wind' or 'air'.)

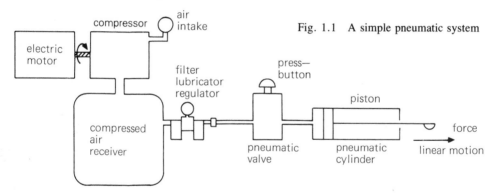

Fig. 1.1   A simple pneumatic system

In industry, atmospheric air is compressed by a special pump called a **compressor** which is driven by a motor. The compressor forces the air into a strong storage tank called a **receiver**. What has happened is that a motor has used, say, electrical energy. This energy has worked the compressor, and most of the energy is now stored in the receiver as compressed air. We have, in fact, a tankful of energy which can do useful work.

■ Social and Industrial Uses of Compressed Air

Every day we come into contact with many devices that work from compressed air. The pneumatic tyre on a motor car is filled with compressed air from the compressors kept in most garages. A garage may have several **air tools**, such as drills, tools to tighten or loosen the nuts on car wheels, and paint sprays, that work from compressed air. Compressed air is used to power a **pneumatic drill** for road repair and building construction work. Dentists use a compressed air drill for the high speed drilling of teeth. The **doors** on tube trains, coaches and buses may be operated pneumatically. **Pneumatic brakes** are common on railway trains, and air assisted brakes are available on many commercial vehicles. Some old-fashioned motor cars had pneumatically operated windscreen wipers. **Pneumatic suspension** systems are used on some modern motor cars.

Fig. 1.2 (a) A pneumatic drill
(b) A dentist's drill

1 What is the difference between the motion of a pneumatic drill and the motion of a dentist's drill?

In industry, pneumatic components are commonly used in **automation systems** and on production lines. They make possible many automatic production processes such as materials handling, component machining, assembly and packaging. In many manual production processes, the control and safety systems make use of pneumatic devices.

6

Fig. 1.3
Pneumatic control
of a container
filling machine

Fig. 1.4
Pneumatic hoist in
a degreasing plant

This book is concerned with pneumatic devices, how
they are used in circuits, and the application of those
circuits to solve practical problems.

Fig. 1.5   A pneumatically automated lathe

Fig. 1.6 'Why do it yourself . . . when it can be done with air?'

| pull | push | lift | close | open |
| remove | hold fast | operate | feed | squeeze |

■ Pneumatic Circuits and Symbols

In pneumatic circuit diagrams, symbols are used to show the components required, and how they are to be connected. These are the **BSI/ISO** symbols for pneumatic components (BSI = British Standard Institute; ISO = International Organisation for Standardisation). It is essential to learn each new component symbol as it appears.

■ The Single-acting Cylinder

The most important pneumatic components are **valves** and **cylinders**. The valves control the cylinders. The cylinders produce **force** and **linear motion** to do whatever work is required.

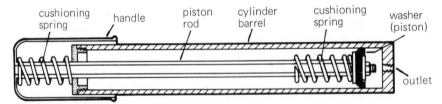

Fig. 1.7   The bicycle pump

Figure 1.7 shows a pneumatic device, a bicycle pump. Study its parts and construction. If air is blown into the outlet end of the pump, the handle will move to the left. A bicycle pump used in this manner is similar to a pneumatic **single-acting cylinder** (Fig. 1.8).

Fig. 1.8   A single-acting cylinder (schematic diagram)

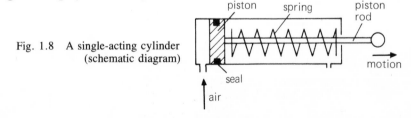

8

Compressed air is fed into the cylinder barrel. The pressure of the air acting on the surface of a special washer, called a **piston**, creates a force. The force moves the piston down the cylinder barrel. Attached to the piston is a piston rod, which passes through the end of the cylinder barrel. As the piston moves down the cylinder, the piston rod moves out of the end of the cylinder. When the compressed air supply is turned off, a spring pushes the piston back down the cylinder.

Fig. 1.9   A midget single-acting cylinder

Fig. 1.10   Circuit diagram symbol for the single-acting cylinder

The BSI/ISO symbol for a single-acting cylinder is shown in Fig. 1.10.

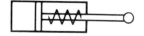

■ Applications of the Single-acting Cylinder

The single-acting cylinder is mainly used for light applications where great force is not required and the linear motion is small.

2 Which stroke of the single-acting cylinder gives the greater force: that caused by compressed air or that caused by the spring?

The single-acting cylinder can be used in many applications. Some of these are shown in Fig. 1.11. Study these applications carefully, and discuss their advantages and disadvantages for practical projects.

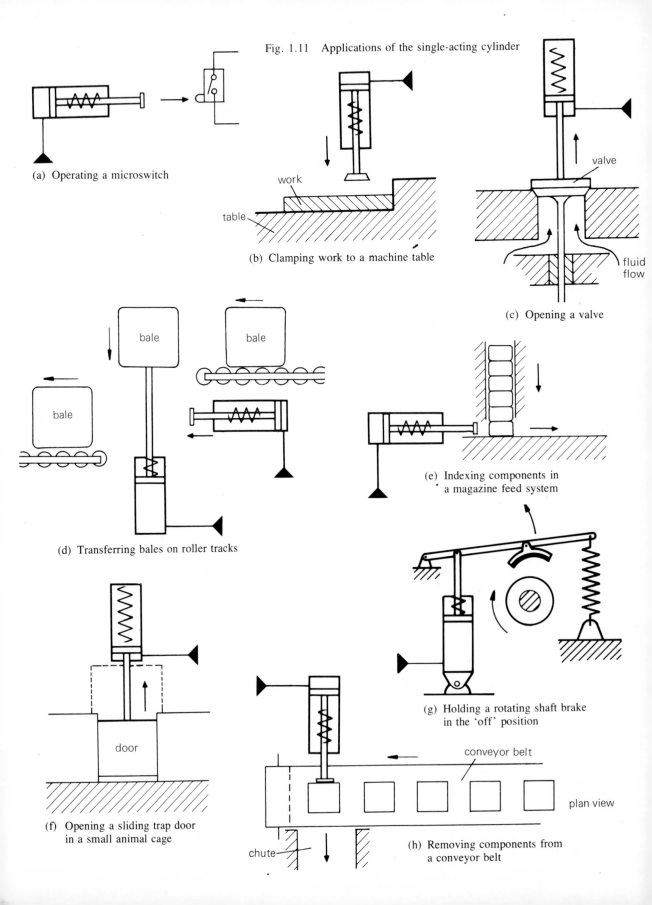

Fig. 1.11   Applications of the single-acting cylinder

(a) Operating a microswitch

(b) Clamping work to a machine table

work

table

(c) Opening a valve

valve

fluid flow

(d) Transferring bales on roller tracks

bale

bale

bale

(e) Indexing components in a magazine feed system

(f) Opening a sliding trap door in a small animal cage

door

(g) Holding a rotating shaft brake in the 'off' position

conveyor belt

plan view

chute

(h) Removing components from a conveyor belt

■ Control of the Single-acting Cylinder – the 3-port Valve

Compressed air is admitted to a single-acting cylinder by a valve. A simple valve is an on/off tap, similar to a gas tap. An on/off tap cannot be used to control a single-acting cylinder. Figure 1.12 shows why.

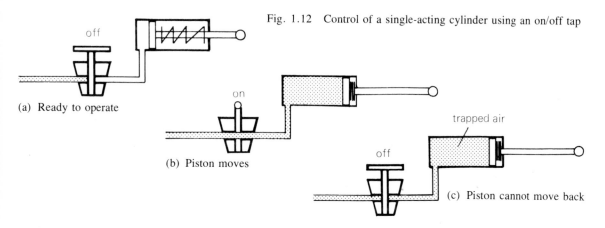

Fig. 1.12   Control of a single-acting cylinder using an on/off tap

(a) Ready to operate

(b) Piston moves

(c) Piston cannot move back

When the tap is turned off again (Fig. 1.12c), compressed air is trapped behind the piston. The spring cannot push the piston back until this air has been removed. A special valve is needed which, when it is turned off, will allow the trapped air to exhaust to the atmosphere. This special valve is called a **3-port valve**. It has one port to which the supply from the compressed air main is connected; a second port to which the cylinder is connected; and a third port through which air in the cylinder can exhaust to the atmosphere when the valve is turned off.

The **main air** supply is represented by the symbol ⊙—

The **exhaust air** is represented by →▶

The **cylinder connection** is represented by ——.

When a 3-port valve is 'on', the air flow pattern through it is represented by the symbol

This shows the exhaust route shut off; main air can pass through.

When a 3-port valve is 'off', the air flow pattern through it is presented by the symbol

The main air route is shut off; the exhaust air can pass through.

These two symbols are put together to form one basic flow pattern symbol for a 3-port valve:

11

The complete symbol is usually drawn showing the 'off' state.

Three-port valves can be turned on and off by a variety of mechanisms.

For example, a valve could be turned on by a push-button 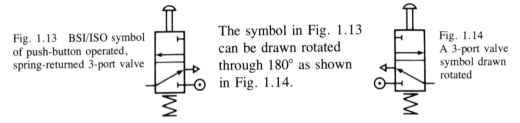 and turned off by a spring

The symbols for these mechanisms are added to the basic flow pattern symbol. They are always added to the half of the basic flow pattern symbol which they cause, i.e. as the push-button turns the valve 'on', its symbol is added to the 'on' flow pattern. As the spring turns the valve 'off', its symbol is added to the 'off' flow pattern. Figure 1.13 shows the complete symbol for a push-button operated, spring-returned 3-port valve.

Fig. 1.13 BSI/ISO symbol of push-button operated, spring-returned 3-port valve

The symbol in Fig. 1.13 can be drawn rotated through 180° as shown in Fig. 1.14.

Fig. 1.14 A 3-port valve symbol drawn rotated

On new 3-port valves, the **ports** (or threaded holes) are marked with the numbers 1, 2 and 3 (Fig. 1.15a and b). Main air is connected to port 1 of the valve. The cylinder is connected to port 2. Exhaust air can escape through port 3.

Fig. 1.15   (a) Push-button operated, spring-returned 3-port valve

(b) Symbol showing numbered ports

(c) Symbol showing lettered ports

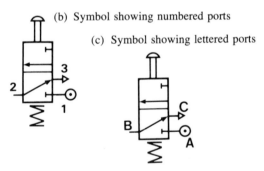

Older valves have the ports marked with letters rather than numbers (Fig. 1.15c). The main air is connected to port A. The cylinder is connected to port B. Exhaust air, returning from a cylinder, can escape through the exhaust port C.

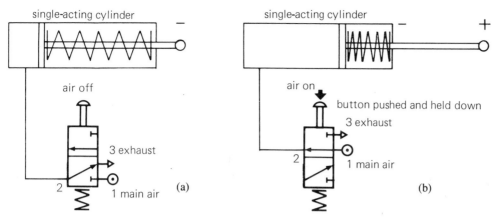

Fig. 1.16   Control of a single-acting cylinder by a push-button operated, spring-returned 3-port valve

The single-acting cylinder is connected to the 3-port valve by nylon tubing (Fig. 1.16). When the button of the 3-port valve is pressed, compressed air flows through the valve and into the cylinder. This causes the piston rod to move out of the cylinder. The piston is said to go positive (+) or outstroke. When the button is released, the force of the spring returns the piston. The air behind the piston escapes to the atmosphere through the exhaust port of the 3-port valve. When the piston rod is retracted into the cylinder, it is said to be negative (−) or instroke.

It is essential to be able to work easily from a circuit diagram to components, and back again from components to a circuit diagram. You must know your equipment and understand circuit diagrams.

  *3 When the button of the 3-port valve is pressed and the cylinder goes posi-
    tive, what happens to the air on the spring side of the piston?*

☐ The 3-port Valve in Detail

A push-button operated, spring-returned 3-port valve has been used in diagrams up to now. Inside the valve there is a small piston, and underneath it is a light spring. When your finger pushes the valve button, this depresses a poppet piston which allows air to flow from port 1, through the valve and out of port 2. If you release your finger from the button, the spring returns the poppet piston and shuts off the supply of air from port 1. The poppet piston is hollow and it will allow exhaust air to pass through itself and out of port 3 (Fig. 1.17).

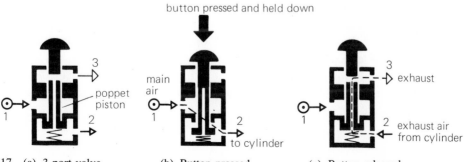

Fig. 1.17   (a) 3-port valve   (b) Button pressed   (c) Button released

Fig. 1.18   Air paths through a 3-port valve to a single-acting cylinder

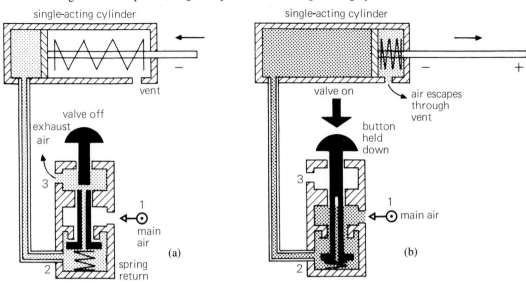

Figure 1.18 shows how the push-button operated 3-port valve can be used to control a single-acting cylinder. When the button is in the 'off' position (Fig. 1.18a), the spring-return on the valve holds the poppet piston tight against a seal, shutting off the main air flow from port 1. The piston in the single-acting cylinder is negative, since it is forced back by the spring in the cylinder. Air trapped behind the returning piston flows into the valve at port 2, through the centre of the poppet piston, to escape through the exhaust port 3. When the button is pushed, the poppet piston is forced down against the spring, breaking the poppet piston seal. Main air from port 1 flows through to port 2 and out to the single-acting cylinder. The pressure of the air acting on the area of the piston forces the piston to go positive or outstroke. As it outstrokes, the piston compresses the cylinder spring. Air trapped in front of the piston escapes to the atmosphere through a vent in the front end of the cylinder.

■ Component Details

Air passes into and out of cylinders and valves through ports. A port is a hole in the device in which there is usually a screw thread. The solenoid valves in the Pneumatics kit have exhaust ports which are simply shrouded vents. The ports of the equipment in the kit are threaded either ⅛″ BSP or ¼″ BSP (BSP = British Standard Pipe thread). Each port of each item of equipment must be fitted with a 'Plasticon' port adaptor of the appropriate size (Fig. 1.19a). The only exceptions to this requirement are the exhaust ports of the valves. These do not normally have port adaptors. The only times when they are required to have port adaptors are clearly indicated.

Fig. 1.19 'Plasticon' tube fittings

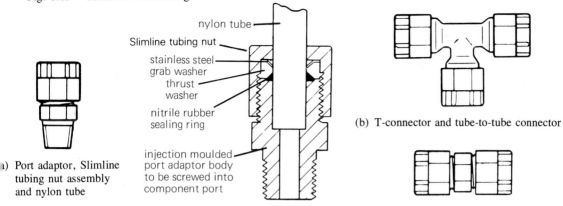

nylon tube

Slimline tubing nut

stainless steel grab washer

thrust washer

nitrile rubber sealing ring

injection moulded port adaptor body to be screwed into component port

(b) T-connector and tube-to-tube connector

(a) Port adaptor, Slimline tubing nut assembly and nylon tube

Nylon tube, 5 mm o.d., is used to connect valves and cylinders together. At each end of each nylon tube there is a Plasticon Slimline nut assembly (Fig. 1.19a). The nut assembly is screwed, finger-tight, on to a port adaptor to make interconnections. A rubber sealing O-ring in the nut assembly ensures an airtight seal between the nylon tube and the port adaptor. Always check that the O-ring is in place on the nylon tube.

A T-connector (Fig. 1.19b) is used to divide a tube into two branches. If three or more branches are required, two or more T-connectors are used together. To join two short tubes to make one long one, a tube-to-tube connector is used (Fig. 1.19b).

Three-port valves are available with several different operating mechanisms, for example, roller-trip and plunger (Fig. 1.20) as well as push-button. The return mechanism for these valves is a spring. In the practical work, any of these spring-return 3-port valves will often be a suitable alternative to the one shown in a circuit diagram.

Fig. 1.20   (a) Roller-trip operated 3-port valve   (b) Plunger operated 3-port valve   (c) Symbol for roller-trip valve

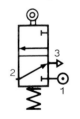

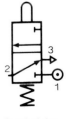

(d) Symbol for plunger operated valve

Single-acting cylinders can be obtained with the piston held instroke by a spring, or with the piston held outstroke by a spring (see Fig. 1.21). The intended application determines the type used.

Fig. 1.21   (a) Sprung instroke single-acting cylinder   (b) Sprung outstroke single-acting cylinder

■ Controlling a Single-acting Cylinder from Two Positions

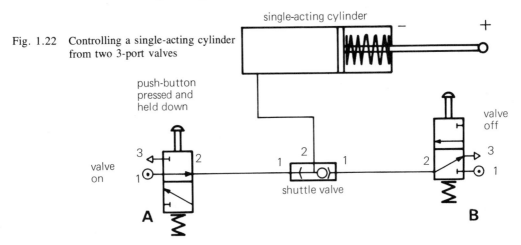

Fig. 1.22   Controlling a single-acting cylinder from two 3-port valves

It is often necessary to control a single-acting cylinder from two positions. To achieve this using two 3-port valves, an extra component called a **shuttle valve** (Fig. 1.23) is required in the circuit. An ordinary T-connector cannot be used to connect two 3-port valves to the single-acting cylinder. This is because, when the button of valve *A* is pressed, the main air released by it would exhaust through valve *B*'s exhaust port rather than make the single-acting cylinder go positive. The shuttle valve routes the air from valve *A* to the single-acting cylinder, and closes off the route to the exhaust port of valve *B* (Fig. 1.22).

Inside the shuttle valve (Fig. 1.23*c*) is a small disc. When an air signal appears on one side of the shuttle valve, the disc moves to the opposite side and seals the other inlet.

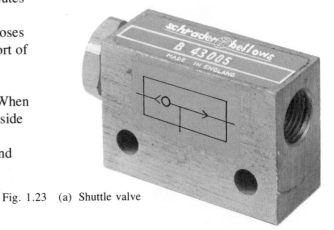

Fig. 1.23   (a) Shuttle valve

16

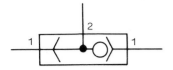 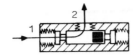 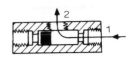

(b) ISO symbol of shuttle valve   (c) Air routes through shuttle valve

If valve *A* in Fig. 1.22 was released and valve *B* pressed, the disc in the shuttle valve would seal the inlet from valve *A* and allow air to the single-acting cylinder from valve *B*.

Answers to Questions

1 A pneumatic drill produces reciprocating motion and a dentist's drill produces rotary motion.

2 That caused by compressed air.

3 It is released to the atmosphere through a hole in the front of the single-acting cylinder.

2 Linear Motion

■ Units of Pressure

A pneumatic cylinder is capable of producing a 'push' or a 'pull' force. **Force** is measured in the SI unit called the **newton** (**N**). As the SI unit of length is the metre, the unit of surface **area** is the **square metre** (**m²**). If a force of one newton is applied over a surface area of one square metre, there is said to be a pressure of one newton per square metre (1 N/m²). One newton per square metre is called one pascal. The **pascal** (**Pa**) is the SI unit of pressure.

In pneumatics, air pressures are high and their values can involve large numbers. For example, the air supplied to pneumatic cylinders could be at a pressure of 500 000 Pa (500 000 N/m²). The problem of large numbers can be overcome by using the millimetre (mm) as the unit of length. This will give surface areas in square millimetres (mm²). If a force of one newton is applied over a surface area of one square millimetre, there is said to be a pressure of one newton per square millimetre (1 N/mm²). The air supplied to pneumatic cylinders could be at a pressure of 0.5 N/mm², which is equivalent to 500 000 N/m². This non-preferred SI unit of pressure, **newtons per square millimetre** (**N/mm²**), will be used in pneumatics calculations in this module.

■ Force from a Pneumatic Cylinder

The force produced by a pneumatic cylinder depends on two things:
1 the pressure at which compressed air is supplied;
2 the surface area of the piston (Fig. 2.1).

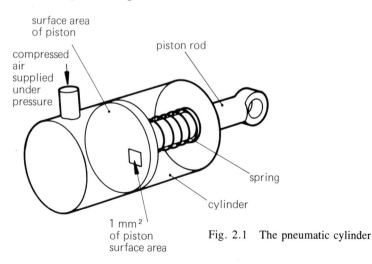

Fig. 2.1   The pneumatic cylinder

18

If the compressed air is supplied at a pressure of 0.5 N/mm², this means that every square millimetre of the piston's surface area has a force of 0.5 N acting over it. If the total number of square millimetres of piston surface area is multiplied by 0.5 N, the answer is the total force acting over the whole surface area of the piston. This can be expressed quite simply as

$$\textbf{force} = \textbf{pressure} \times \textbf{area.}$$

Force produced by cylinder (N) = air pressure (N/mm²) × piston area (mm²).

Example 1

A design engineer needs to know the force produced by a cylinder with a bore diameter of 20 mm when supplied with air at a pressure of 0.5 N/mm².
Note Bore diameter = piston diameter.

$$\text{Area of piston} = \pi r^2 \text{ (where } r \text{ is the radius of the piston)}$$
$$= \pi 10^2 \text{ mm}^2.$$

Using the equation

$$\text{force} = \text{pressure} \times \text{area,}$$
$$\text{force} = 0.5 \times \pi 10^2 \text{ N}$$
$$= 0.5 \times \pi \times 100 \text{ N}$$
$$= 50\pi \text{ N}$$
$$= 50 \times 3.142 \text{ N.}$$

Therefore, force is 157.1 newtons.

Example 2

A force of 140 newtons is required to move a certain load. The factory air line pressure is 0.7 N/mm². The design engineer needs to know the bore diameter of the pneumatic cylinder which will do the job.

The first step is to calculate the surface area of the piston.

$$\text{As force} = \text{pressure} \times \text{area,}$$
$$\text{area} = \frac{\text{force}}{\text{pressure}}$$
$$= \frac{140}{0.7} \text{ mm}^2.$$

Therefore, piston surface area is 200 mm².
But, as piston surface area also equals πr^2 (where r is the bore radius),

$$\pi r^2 = 200 \text{ mm}^2$$
$$r^2 = \frac{200}{\pi} \text{ mm}^2$$
$$r = \sqrt{\frac{200}{\pi}} \text{ mm.}$$

As bore diameter = $2r$,

$$\text{bore diameter} = 2\sqrt{\frac{200}{\pi}} \text{ mm}$$
$$\simeq 16 \text{ mm.}$$

■ The Compressor Unit

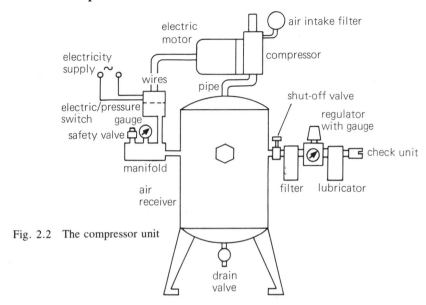

Fig. 2.2   The compressor unit

The compressed air to power pneumatic cylinders is obtained from a compressor unit (Fig. 2.2). Air is drawn in from the atmosphere through a filter into a piston type of pump called a **compressor**. The compressor pumps the air into a steel storage tank called an **air receiver**. The compressor is driven by an electric motor, which is controlled by a pressure switch connected to the air receiver. When the pressure in the air receiver falls to a preset minimum value, the pressure switch turns on the electric motor, and the compressor supplies more air to the receiver. When the air pressure in the receiver reaches a preset maximum value, the pressure switch turns off the electric motor and the compressor stops.

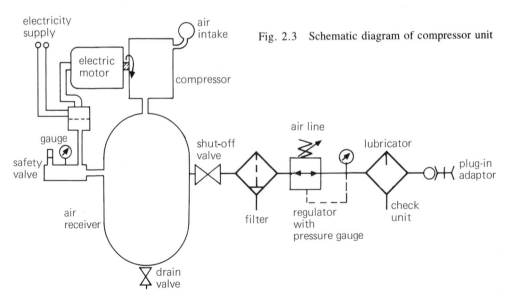

Fig. 2.3   Schematic diagram of compressor unit

When air is compressed, water condenses out of it and collects at the bottom of the air receiver. This water must be drained regularly from the air receiver. A drain valve is fitted at the base of the receiver for this purpose.

A **safety valve** (Fig. 2.4) is connected to the air receiver, and this will release air to the atmosphere should the pressure switch fail.

Fig. 2.4   Safety valve

The pressure in the air receiver is indicated by a **pressure gauge** connected to the receiver (Fig. 2.5).

Fig. 2.5   Pressure gauge

Pressure gauges are often calibrated in a unit of pressure called the 'bar'. One bar is approximately atmospheric pressure, i.e. about $0.1 \, \text{N/mm}^2$ (one bar is approximately $10^5 \, \text{N/m}^2$). The pressure gauge on a compressor might show a reading of 5 bar (Fig. 2.6).

Fig. 2.6   Units of pressure – approximate equivalents

When air leaves the receiver, it passes through a shut-off valve. Before it reaches the air line it passes through a **filter unit** (Fig. 2.7). This removes moisture from the air so that pneumatic equipment will not become rusted. The air then passes to a **pressure regulator** (Fig. 2.8) fitted with a pressure gauge. The air in the receiver is at a higher pressure than the equipment requires. The regulator supplies the equipment with air at a steady, but lower, pressure. This pressure can be adjusted by turning the control knob.

Fig. 2.7   Filter

Fig. 2.8   Regulator with gauge

Some air lines have a **lubricator** unit included (Fig. 2.9). Whilst this is not essential for schools, it does lubricate the pneumatic components and prolong their life. The lubricator introduces a fine mist of light oil into the compressed air.

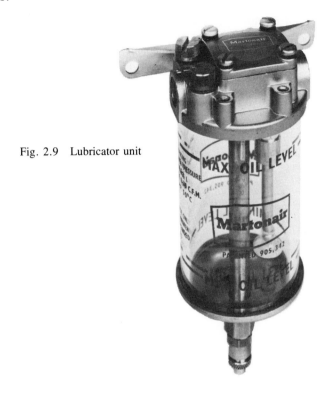

Fig. 2.9   Lubricator unit

The air now enters the distribution system, the air line. This is usually galvanised steel tube. At intervals along this tubing, **check units** (Fig. 2.10) are fitted. These enable equipment to be 'plugged into' the air supply, using adaptors which match the check units.

Fig. 2.10   Check unit

■ The Double-acting Cylinder

Unlike the single-acting cylinder, the **double-acting cylinder** has a port at each end. When compressed air is allowed to enter the rear port, it moves the piston forward and the piston rod goes positive. Air in front of the piston exhausts out of the front port. Similarly, if compressed air is injected through the front port, the piston rod moves back into the cylinder. It goes negative. Air behind the piston exhausts through the rear port.

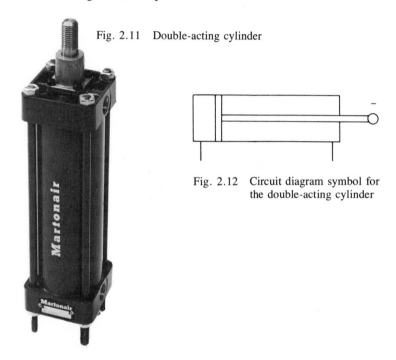

Fig. 2.11   Double-acting cylinder

Fig. 2.12   Circuit diagram symbol for the double-acting cylinder

1 Revision: What returns the piston in a single-acting cylinder?

■ Control of the Double-acting Cylinder

Fig. 2.13   3-port valve control of a double-acting cylinder

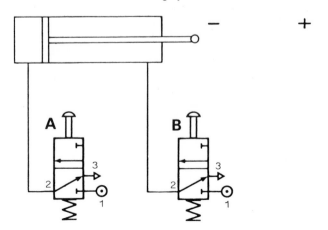

A double-acting cylinder can be controlled by two 3-port valves. Figure 2.13 shows two push-button, spring-return 3-port valves connected to the double-acting cylinder. Since main air is connected to both 3-port valves, the main air supply line has to be divided by a T-connector. When valve A is pressed, the main air is supplied to the double-acting cylinder and the piston rod goes positive. The air in front of the piston escapes through the exhaust route of valve B and exhausts to the atmosphere through port 3. Main air is only supplied to the cylinder while valve A push-button remains pressed. It is cut off as soon as the button is released because this 3-port valve is spring-returned. When the button of valve B is pressed, the double-acting cylinder goes negative. Air behind the piston is exhausted through port 3 of valve A.

2 *What will happen if both valve A and valve B are pressed at the same time?*

■ Five-port Valve Control of a Double-acting Cylinder

In practice, a double-acting cylinder is rarely controlled by two 3-port valves. Usually, it is controlled by one **5-port valve**. A 5-port valve is like two 3-port valves rolled into one. It has two cylinder ports (2 and 4, or B and D), two exhaust ports (3 and 5, or C and E), and one main air port (1 or A). Like the 3-port valve, the 5-port valve has two positions. This means it has two different air flow patterns. One air flow pattern is:

Main air flows in at port 1 and out at port 2. Exhaust air flows in at port 4 and out at port 5. Port 3 is blocked off. The other air flow pattern is:

Main air flows in at port 1 and out at port 4. Exhaust air flows in at port 2 and out at port 3. Port 5 is blocked off. These two air flow patterns are put together to form one basic air flow pattern symbol for a 5-port valve:

The cylinder, main air and exhaust symbols are added only to the left or right half of the basic flow pattern symbol. They are never on both sides at the same time. The choice of left or right half depends on which of the two halves describes what is happening in a circuit. Figure 2.14 shows a lever set/reset 5-port valve. Figure 2.15 shows this valve controlling a double-acting cylinder. Note the valve's circuit diagram symbol.

25

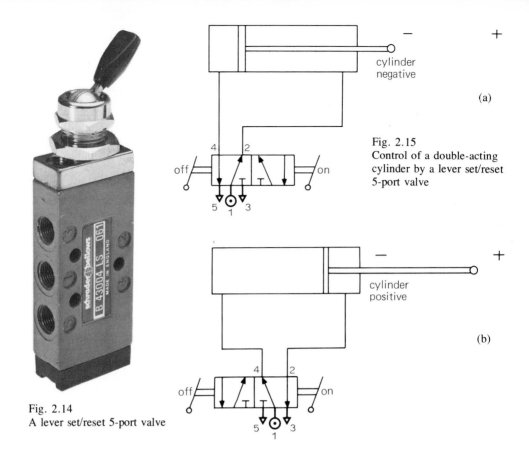

Fig. 2.15
Control of a double-acting cylinder by a lever set/reset 5-port valve

(a)

(b)

cylinder negative

cylinder positive

Fig. 2.14
A lever set/reset 5-port valve

Figure 2.15 shows the two positions of the 5-port valve when controlling a double-acting cylinder. When the 5-port valve is in the 'off' position (Fig. 2.15a), main air enters the valve at port 1. It leaves the valve by port 2 and passes to the cylinder, causing it to go negative. As the cylinder goes negative, exhaust air returns from the cylinder to port 4. It passes through the valve and escapes to the atmosphere by exhaust port 5. If the 5-port valve is switched to the 'on' position (Fig. 2.15b), main air passes through the valve from port 1 to port 4 and passes to the cylinder, causing it to go positive. As it goes positive, exhaust air returns from the cylinder to port 2. It escapes to the atmosphere from exhaust port 3.

3 Can you think of an application for this circuit?

☐ The 5-port Valve in Detail

The 3-port valves used in this course have poppet valves. The type of 5-port valves used have **piston valves.** Inside the 5-port valve is a piston or **spool.** This spool is made of light alloy and is fitted with four O-ring seals made of synthetic rubber. It is connected to the operating mechanism. In the lever set/reset 5-port valve, the hand lever moves the spool into one or other of its two positions.

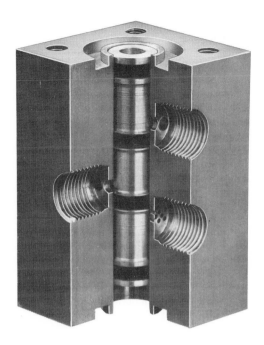

Fig. 2.16 Section through a 5-port valve showing spool and seals

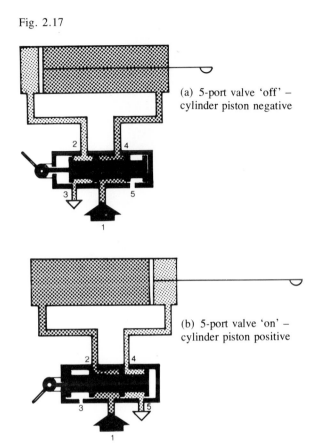

Fig. 2.17

(a) 5-port valve 'off' –
cylinder piston negative

(b) 5-port valve 'on' –
cylinder piston positive

When the operating lever is in the 'on' position (Fig. 2.17b), main air enters the valve through port 1. It leaves the valve from port 2 to go to the cylinder. The cylinder goes positive. As it does so, exhaust air returns from the cylinder to port 4. It passes through the valve and exhausts to atmosphere through port 5. In the 'off' position of the lever, the spool is moved to allow supply air entering the valve at port 1 to leave the valve from port 4 to go to the cylinder. The cylinder goes negative. As it does so, exhaust air returns from the cylinder to port 2 of the valve. It passes through the valve and exhausts to the atmosphere through port 3.

■ **Types of 5-port Valve and Applications**

Apart from the manually operated lever set/reset mechanism, there are several ways in which a 5-port valve can be operated. They include push-button, roller-trip and plunger operated valves, all with spring-returns (Fig. 2.18).

(a) Push-button operated

(c) Plunger operated

Fig. 2.18   A selection of 5-port valves

(b) Roller-trip operated

Fig. 2.19   Symbols for the 5-port valves shown in Fig. 2.18

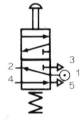

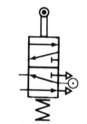

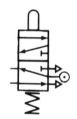

(a) Push-button operated   (b) Roller-trip operated   (c) Plunger operated

There are several methods for mechanically activating these valves. Some are shown in Fig. 2.20.

Fig. 2.20   Mechanical methods of operating a valve

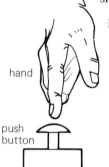

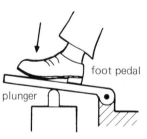

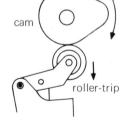

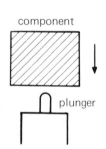

(a) Finger on push-button   (b) Foot-pedal on plunger   (c) Rotating cam on roller-trip   (d) Component on plunger

Each of these 5-port valves can be connected to a double-acting cylinder and used in applications where the piston must return to, and rest in, its starting position after each operation. Some applications are shown in Fig. 2.21.

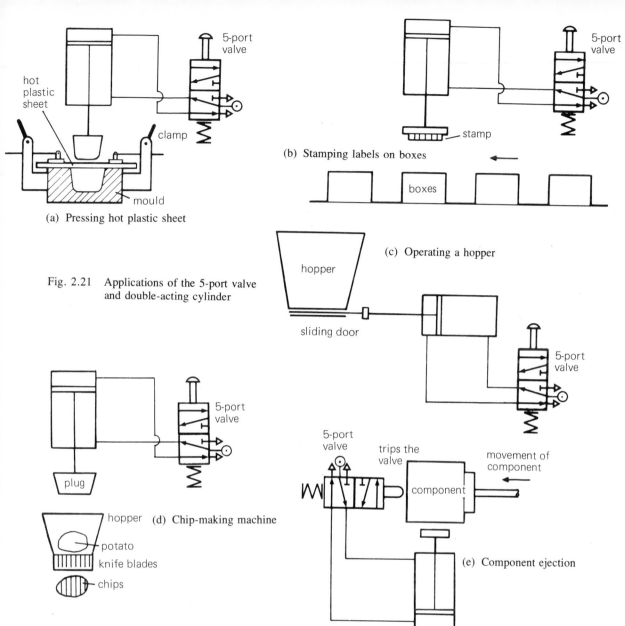

(a) Pressing hot plastic sheet

(b) Stamping labels on boxes

(c) Operating a hopper

Fig. 2.21 Applications of the 5-port valve and double-acting cylinder

(d) Chip-making machine

(e) Component ejection

Answers to Questions

1 A spring.

2 If the piston is in the negative position or in the middle of the cylinder when both valves are pressed, the piston rod will go positive. This is because the piston area on side A is larger than side B. Part of the piston area on side B is lost where the piston rod is fitted to the piston. If the piston is already in the positive position, it will stay positive.

3 Manually operating a clamp or a press tool. The 5-port valve can be obtained with foot-pedal operation. This could be useful in working a clamp, as it leaves the hands free.

3 Cylinders and Valves

■ Controlling Two Cylinders

In some applications it is necessary to operate two or more cylinders from one valve. For example, if two single-acting cylinders are used to work two clamps simultaneously on a machine table, they can be controlled from one valve (Fig. 3.1).

Fig. 3.1   Control of two single-acting cylinders by a 3-port valve

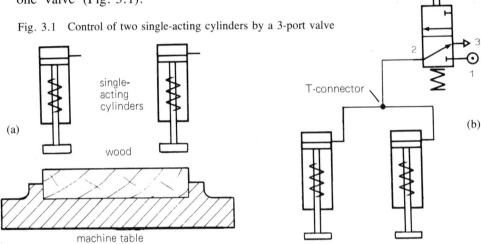

A 3-port valve can be connected to two single-acting cylinders by the use of a T-connector (Fig. 1.19b). The pipes between the T-connector and the cylinders should be of equal length to assist simultaneous operation of the cylinders. In a similar way, it is necessary to use a four-way connector to join three single-acting cylinders to a 3-port valve (Fig. 3.2). A four-way connector can be made by joining two T-connectors with a very short piece of nylon tube.

Fig. 3.2   Control of three single-acting cylinders by a 3-port valve

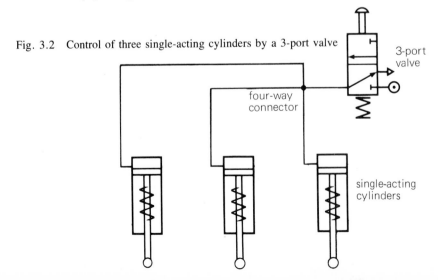

A 5-port valve can be used to control two or more double-acting cylinders. The circuit shown in Fig. 3.3 requires two T-connectors to divide the air supply and exhaust routes.

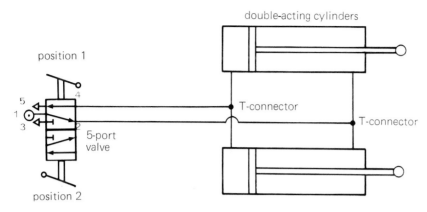

Fig. 3.3   Control of two double-acting cylinders

With the 5-port valve in position 1, both the double-acting cylinders are in the negative (instroke) position. When the 5-port valve is switched to position 2, the double-acting cylinders go positive (outstroke).

   An example of the use of this method of connecting cylinders is shown in Fig. 3.4. Two double-acting cylinders are used to raise and lower a door by using wires and pulleys.

Fig. 3.4   Use of two double-acting cylinders

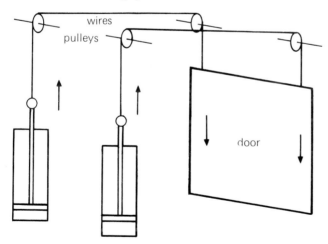

Another arrangement is to begin with one cylinder positive and one cylinder negative (Fig. 3.5). When the 5-port valve is moved to position 2, the negative cylinder will go positive, and the positive cylinder will go negative.

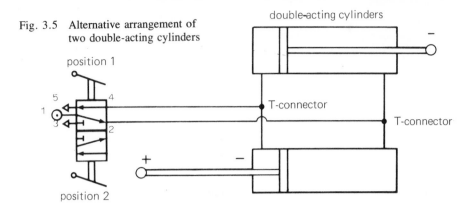

Fig. 3.5 Alternative arrangement of two double-acting cylinders

double-acting cylinders

position 1

position 2

T-connector

T-connector

This circuit could be used to open a furnace door and put an object in the furnace (Fig. 3.6). It may be necessary to operate the furnace door some time before putting in the object. This requires a time delay. Time-delay circuit techniques are described in Chapter 6.

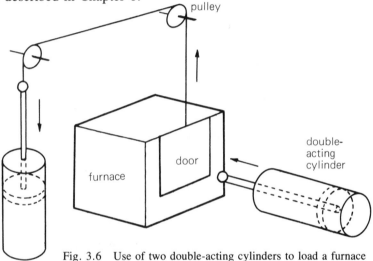

Fig. 3.6 Use of two double-acting cylinders to load a furnace

■ The Single-acting Cylinder and the Double-acting Cylinder

Two kinds of pneumatic cylinder have been used in this course: the single-acting cylinder and the double-acting cylinder.

1 What is the BSI/ISO symbol for the single-acting pneumatic cylinder?

In a single-acting cylinder, compressed air enters behind the piston. The pressure of the air acting on the area of the piston produces a force which pushes the piston rod outwards. When the air is released, a spring returns the piston rod. The spring can be seen in a sectioned view of a single-acting cylinder in Fig. 3.7.

Fig. 3.7 Section through a single-acting cylinder

Fig. 3.8 Section through a double-acting cylinder

In a double-acting cylinder, air can enter either behind or in front of the piston. Air behind the piston moves the piston rod outwards. Air in front of the piston moves the piston rod inwards. For clarity, Fig. 3.8 shows a sectioned view of a simple, non-cushioned double-acting cylinder. In this cylinder, the piston can violently strike the cylinder end caps at the end of either movement. This can cause damage. Cushioning is a design refinement which prevents this happening. An air cushion slows down the piston just before the end of either movement. The cylinders in the Pneumatics kit are **cushioned cylinders**. Figure 1:7 shows the cushioning arrangements for a bicycle pump.

Double-acting cylinders vary in size according to the diameter of their bore and the length of their stroke. The double-acting cylinders in the kit have a range of stroke lengths from 50 mm to 300 mm. The bore or diameter of the cylinders is about 30 mm.

2 What is the BSI/ISO symbol for the double-acting cylinder?

□ The Cushioned Double-acting Cylinder in Detail

The cushioning effect is achieved by a cushion boss on either side of the piston (Fig. 3.9). The boss has a seal which fits into the end cap when the piston almost reaches the end of its stroke.

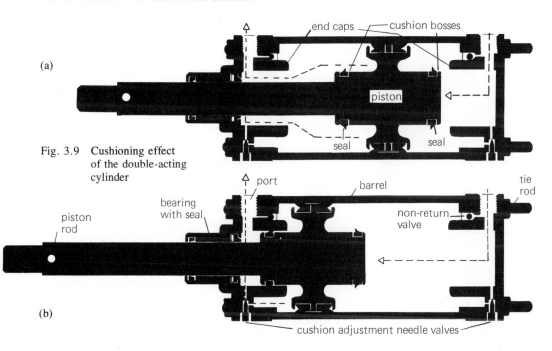

Fig. 3.9   Cushioning effect
of the double-acting
cylinder

The operating principle of the cushioned double-acting cylinder is shown in Fig. 3.9. To move the piston positive from the negative position, main air enters through the rear port. With the piston fully negative, the main air would only act

33

over the small surface area of the end of the cushion boss. This would result in a small initial force and serious operating problems. To overcome this, a non-return valve allows the air to act over the full surface area of the piston. The piston is pushed forward. Air in front of the piston escapes through the front port. Near the end of the piston movement, the cushion boss reaches the recess in the front end cap. The seal on the cushion boss fits into the recess and traps air in front of the piston. This sudden trapping of air arrests the piston movement. This air is the cushion the piston hits. The trapped air escapes slowly through a needle valve in the front end cap. The needle valve can be adjusted to alter the cushioning effect. A similar cushioning effect is achieved on the reverse stroke of the piston (the instroke).

■ **The Double Pressure Operated 5-port Valve**

Many of the pneumatic circuits described in the remainder of this book use a double pressure operated 5-port valve. The **double pressure operated 5-port valve** is operated by air signals rather than by a mechanical mechanism such as a lever or push-button. This valve is shown in Fig. 3.10 without port adaptors. Before it can be used, it must have port adaptors screwed into its ports. The BSI/ISO symbol for the double pressure operated 5-port valve is shown in Fig. 3.11.

Fig. 3.10   The double pressure operated 5-port valve

Fig. 3.11   Symbol for the double pressure operated 5-port valve

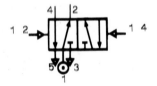

Inside this 5-port valve is a spool which is moved into one of two possible positions by an air signal acting on one or other end of it. The spool moves like a piston in a double-acting cylinder. The ports which receive the air signal are labelled 1 2 and 1 4. The symbols in Fig. 3.12 show the two positions of the double pressure operated 5-port valve.

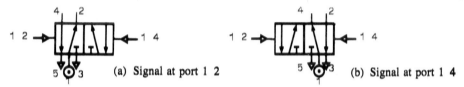

(a) Signal at port 1 2   (b) Signal at port 1 4

Fig. 3.12   Two positions of the double pressure operated 5-port valve

In the first position, an air signal appears at the signal port 1 2. The main supply air enters the valve at port 1 and leaves the valve at port 2.

In the second position, an air signal appears at the signal port 1 4. The main supply air enters the valve at port 1 and leaves the valve at port 4.

You should try to remember:
An air signal at signal port 1 2 gives main air out of port 2.
An air signal at signal port 1 4 gives main air out of port 4.

☐ **The Double Pressure Operated 5-port Valve in Detail**

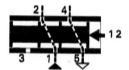

Fig. 3.13   Spool positions of the double pressure operated 5-port valve

(a) When the piston is in this position, the supply air is taken to the inlet port 1 and connected to the cylinder port 2. The exhausting air passes from cylinder port 4 to exhaust port 5.

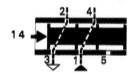

(b) When the valve is operated, the piston moves to the other end of the valve, the supply air is connected to port 4, and the exhausting air passes from port 2 to port 3.

Inside a double pressure operated 5-port valve is a light metal spool or piston with four sealing O-rings (Fig. 2.16). An air signal applied to the end of the piston will move it along the 5-port valve. Because force produced = air pressure × piston area, air pressure on the left-hand end (1 4) of the valve piston (Fig. 3.13b) causes a force which moves the piston towards the right. With the piston in this position, the main supply air passes through inlet port 1 and out of cylinder port 4. The exhausting air passes from port 2 and exhausts from port 3. If an air signal is applied to the right-hand end (1 2) of the valve piston (Fig. 3.13a), the pressure acting on the piston area produces a force to move the piston towards the left. With the valve piston in this position, the main supply air passes through the inlet port 1 and out of cylinder port 2. The exhausting air passes from port 4 and exhausts from port 5.

If air signals of equal pressure are applied at each end of the valve at the same time, the valve piston remains stationary because the forces on each end are equal. A double pressure operated 5-port valve cannot respond to two signals from both sides at the same time.

■ Control of a Double-acting Cylinder by One Pilot Valve

Double pressure operated 5-port valves are often used to control double-acting cylinders. Hence they are sometimes called **control valves.** Engineers normally want to signal the control valve from a remote point. The signalling can be achieved by using one **pilot valve.** The pilot valve is also a 5-port valve and could be worked by a range of different operating mechanisms. The pilot valve produces an air signal which operates the control valve. The control valve operates the cylinder. Figure 3.14 shows a block diagram of the complete system.

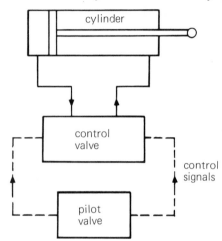

Fig. 3.14   Block diagram of pneumatic circuit with pilot valve control of a double-acting cylinder

Pilot valve control can be achieved by signalling a double pressure operated 5-port valve from a remote point by a lever set/reset 5-port valve. Figure 3.15 shows this pneumatic circuit with the cylinder in both the positive and negative positions.

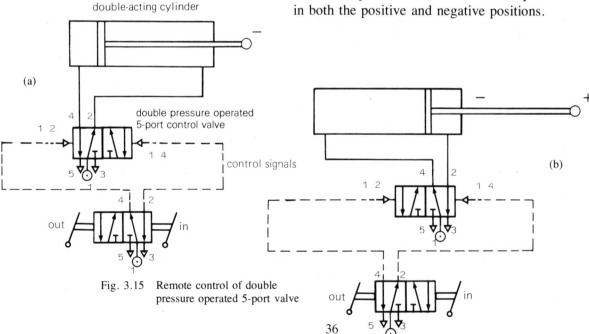

Fig. 3.15   Remote control of double pressure operated 5-port valve

In circuits involving pilot valves (like the circuit in Fig. 3.15) the control signal pipes between the pilot valve and the control valve are shown as **broken lines**. Air pipes between the control valve and the cylinder are indicated by **continuous lines**.

Consider Fig. 3.15a. With the 5-port pilot valve in the 'in' position, main air enters the pilot valve at port 1 and leaves from port 4. This air provides a signal at the 1 2 signal port of the double pressure operated 5-port control valve. Main air from port 2 of the control valve keeps the cylinder piston negative. When the 5-port pilot valve is switched to the 'out' position (Fig. 3.15b), the air signal is removed from signal port 1 2 and placed on signal port 1 4 of the control valve. An air signal at signal port 1 4 means the spool in the valve is switched. Air leaves the control valve from port 4. This makes the cylinder piston go positive.

■ **Control of a Double-acting Cylinder by Two Pilot Valves**

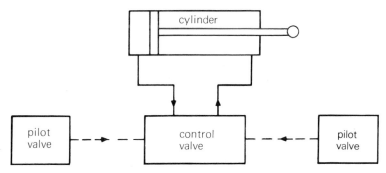

Fig. 3.16   Block diagram of pilot valve control of a double-acting cylinder

Pilot valve control of a double-acting cylinder can also be achieved with two pilot valves (Fig. 3.16). The control valve is a double pressure operated 5-port valve, and the pilot valves are spring-return 3-port valves which could be push-button operated (Fig. 3.17).

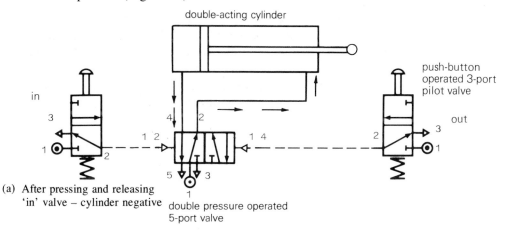

(a) After pressing and releasing 'in' valve – cylinder negative

Fig. 3.17   Pilot valve control of a double-acting cylinder

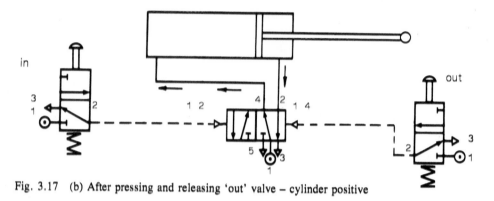

Fig. 3.17 (b) After pressing and releasing 'out' valve – cylinder positive

When the 'in' 3-port pilot valve is pressed and released, an air signal is sent to signal port 1 2 of the double pressure operated 5-port control valve. Consequently, main air leaves the control valve at port 2 and the cylinder piston moves negative. As the 3-port pilot valve is a spring-return valve, the air signal is removed when the push-button is released.

If the 'out' 3-port pilot valve is pressed, an air signal appears at signal port 1 4 of the control valve. The spool of the valve switches, allowing air out of port 4. This main air moves the piston positive.

Circuit diagrams show what has just happened in a circuit. For example, in Fig. 3.17a, the piston has just gone negative. The piston could do this because the left-hand flow pattern of the 5-port valve symbol was set up. This flow pattern was set up when the 'in' 3-port valve was operated. This 3-port valve was released immediately after operation and is shown in its normal 'at rest' position. When drawing a circuit diagram, it is important that all the symbols agree in this manner or the drawing will not make sense.

The circuit shown in Fig. 3.17 is the foundation of much of the remainder of the work in this book. It must be studied and fully understood.

■ An Application of Remote Pilot Valve Control

Pilot valves are often used to control a double-acting cylinder from a remote position. When a process is dangerous or when it is difficult for the operator to get close to the cylinder, then remote control is a solution to the problem. For example, a person might have to dip a basket of components into a bath of corrosive or degreasing liquid. The basket can be raised and lowered by a double-acting cylinder. Remote control can be obtained by the use of pilot valves. This is shown in Fig. 3.18.

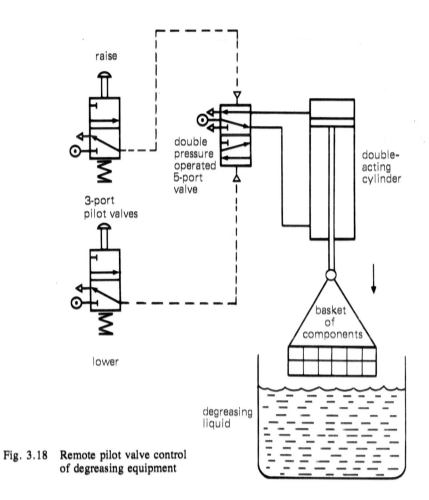

raise

3-port
pilot valves

lower

double
pressure
operated
5-port
valve

double-
acting
cylinder

basket
of
components

degreasing
liquid

Fig. 3.18   Remote pilot valve control
            of degreasing equipment

Answers to Questions
1 BSI/ISO symbol for the single-acting cylinder

2 BSI/ISO symbol for the double-acting cylinder

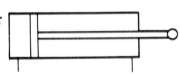

4 Piston Speed Control

■ Introduction

In many applications it is necessary to control the speed at which a piston moves in a cylinder. Control may be necessary in one direction only. Sometimes the piston speed is controlled on both the outstroke and instroke. Control is achieved by regulating the rate at which exhausting air can leave a cylinder. The exhausting air is regulated by a **unidirectional flow control valve**, or **flow regulator** (Fig. 4.1).

Fig. 4.1   The flow regulator – unidirectional flow control valve

Air can flow either way through a flow regulator. If air enters the device at port 1 and leaves at port 2 (*A* and *B* on older devices) its rate of flow can be increased or decreased by turning the knurled adjusting screw. If air flows the other way, entering at port 2 and leaving at port 1, the adjusting screw has no effect and the air flows freely. The circuit diagram symbol for a flow regulator is shown in Fig. 4.2.

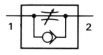

Fig. 4.2   The BSI/ISO symbol for the flow regulator

□ The Flow Regulator in Detail

In Fig. 4.3*a*, air flows from port 2 to port 1. The air pressure overcomes a spring holding a non-return valve closed. The non-return valve is lifted off its seating. Air can now bypass the adjustable needle and flow freely through the device.

Fig. 4.3   Cross-section of a flow regulator

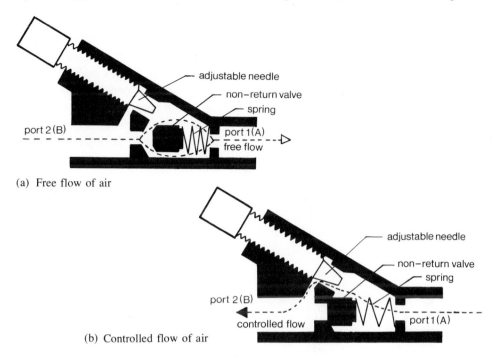

(a) Free flow of air

(b) Controlled flow of air

In Fig. 4.3*b*, air flows from port 1 to port 2. A spring and the air pressure keep the non-return valve closed. Air can only flow past the adjustable needle. The rate of flow depends on the position of the needle.

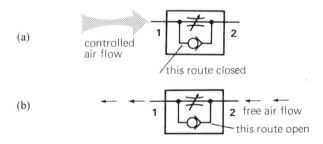

Fig. 4.4   Air flow direction and the flow regulator symbol

In Fig. 4.4 it can be seen that the symbol reflects how the flow regulator works. The two arcs indicate a restriction in the air passage, while the sloping arrow through the arcs indicates that the restriction is adjustable. The non-return valve, and the way it seals, is indicated with a bypass which contains a ball and seat. There is a free flow of air from port 2 to port 1, and an adjustable flow of air from port 1 to port 2.

41

■ Controlling Piston Speed

Speed control is achieved by regulating the rate at which air can exhaust from a cylinder. It is not good practice to regulate the rate at which main air is supplied to a cylinder. When running cylinders unloaded on a bench, it appears to make no difference whether exhaust or supply air is regulated. It does make a difference when the cylinder is working against a fluctuating load, as this causes changes in piston speed. The time taken for the piston speed to regain its preset value is much shorter when exhaust air is regulated than when supply air is regulated. Care must be taken to connect a flow regulator in the right place and the right way round.

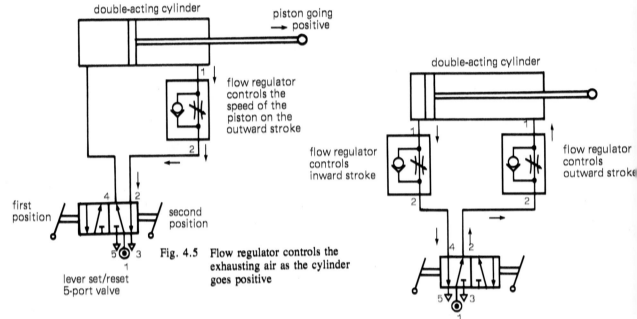

Fig. 4.5   Flow regulator controls the exhausting air as the cylinder goes positive

Fig. 4.6   Flow regulators control piston speed on both outward and inward strokes

Consider the control of a double-acting cylinder with a 5-port valve, as shown in Fig. 4.5. When the 5-port valve is switched to the second position, the main supply air causes the piston to begin to move positive. The air in front of the piston starts to exhaust through the flow regulator. The exhausting air cannot flow out freely, as it is being controlled by the flow regulator. This creates a back pressure against which the piston has to operate. The speed of the piston movement is therefore slowed down.

When the valve is switched to the first position, the piston moves negative rapidly. Air passes freely through the regulator to the cylinder. To control the instroke speed, a second flow regulator is required (Fig. 4.6).

If flow regulators are placed in both air lines between the valve and cylinder, the piston speed is controlled on both the outward and inward strokes. Piston speed is reduced by closing down the adjusting needles of the flow regulators. A fully open flow regulator will allow maximum piston speed. Flow regulators should be placed as near the cylinder as possible.

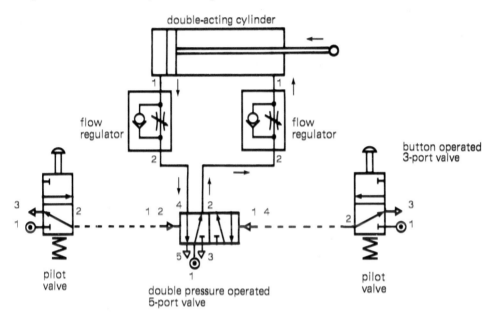

Fig. 4.7   Flow regulators control piston speed in a circuit using pilot valves to operate a double-acting cylinder

In a circuit where the cylinder is remotely controlled by pilot valves, the flow regulators are again placed close to the cylinder (Fig. 4.7). The flow regulators control the piston speed by regulating the rate of flow of the exhausting air.

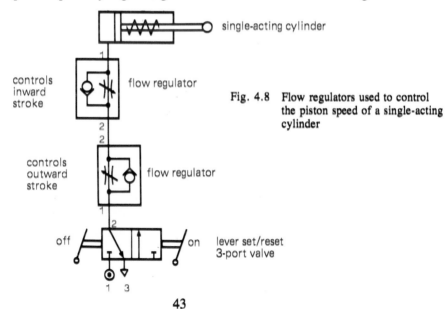

Fig. 4.8   Flow regulators used to control the piston speed of a single-acting cylinder

43

A single-acting cylinder can be controlled by a lever set/reset 3-port valve. In order to control the piston speed, it is necessary to use two flow regulators back to back (Fig. 4.8). As the piston moves outward, its speed is controlled by the flow regulator closest to the 3-port valve. This regulates the rate of flow of air into the cylinder. When the main supply air is turned off, the cylinder spring returns the piston. The piston speed is controlled by the flow regulator closest to the single-acting cylinder. This regulates the rate of flow of air exhausting from the cylinder.

■ Applications of Circuits with Control of Piston Speed

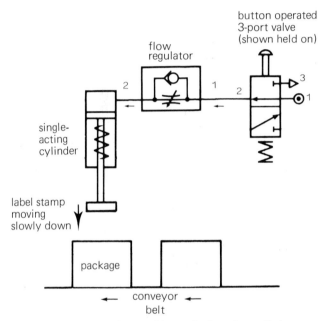

Fig. 4.9   Label stamping machine – single-acting cylinder

Figure 4.9 shows an example of the use of a single-acting cylinder with controlled piston speed. It is a simple machine for stamping labels on fragile packages. As the packages pass along a conveyor belt, a stamp slowly decends and labels each one. The outward stroke of the single-acting cylinder is slow and smooth so that the fragile contents of the package are not damaged. The spring can return the piston quickly after stamping the package. A flow regulator is used in the air line between the 3-port valve and the single-acting cylinder. In this example, air flow is regulated as it enters the cylinder. It is an example of **in-line speed control**. In applications where double-acting cylinders are used, it is usual to control the flow of the exhausting air, as this produces smooth, constant speed control.

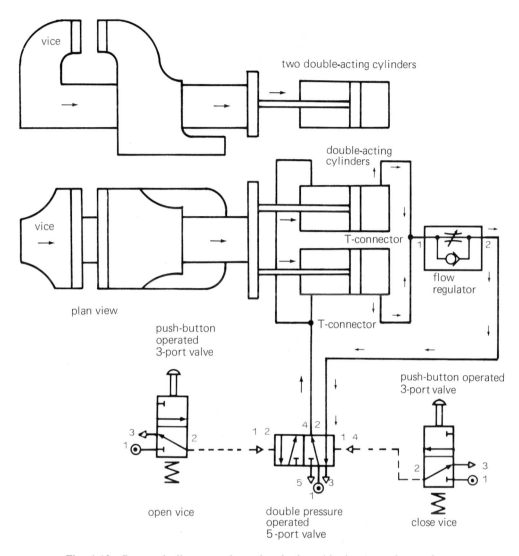

Fig. 4.10   Pneumatically operated metalwork vice with piston speed control

A vice operated pneumatically is an application that requires piston speed control in one direction. The vice is operated by two double-acting cylinders (Fig. 4.10). These cylinders work simultaneously. For safety reasons, it is necessary to close the vice slowly. This also allows the user to carefully position work in the vice. The vice can be opened quickly by pressing a button operated 3-port valve. To achieve control of the pistons' speed when the vice is closing, a flow regulator is connected in the exhaust air line. This is an example of **exhaust speed control**. To be most effective, the flow regulator should be placed as near the cylinders as possible.

Fig. 4.11   Pneumatic system for operating a greenhouse window

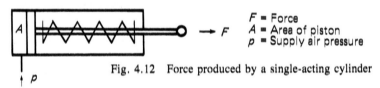

A circuit that requires piston speed control in both directions is shown in Fig. 4.11. A double-acting cylinder could be used to open the roof light or window of a greenhouse. The piston movement must be slow and smooth, as sudden or rapid movement would probably break the glass. The double-acting cylinder is pivoted at both ends to ensure correct linkage movement. Two flow regulators control the piston speed for both the instroke and the outstroke of the cylinder. Smooth piston movement is obtained by regulating the flow of air exhausting from the cylinder.

☐ **Cylinder Force**

Fig. 4.12   Force produced by a single-acting cylinder

In Chapter 2 we saw that the force produced by a single-acting cylinder (ignoring the spring) is given by:

force = pressure of supply air × area of piston.

Force is measured in newtons (N). Pressure is measured in newtons per mm². Area is measured in mm².

It is more difficult to calculate the outstroke force produced by a double-acting cylinder because there is pressure on both sides of the piston (Fig. 4.13).

Fig. 4.13   Force produced by a double-acting cylinder

F = Force
A = Area of piston
p_1 = Inlet pressure
p_2 = Exhausting pressure

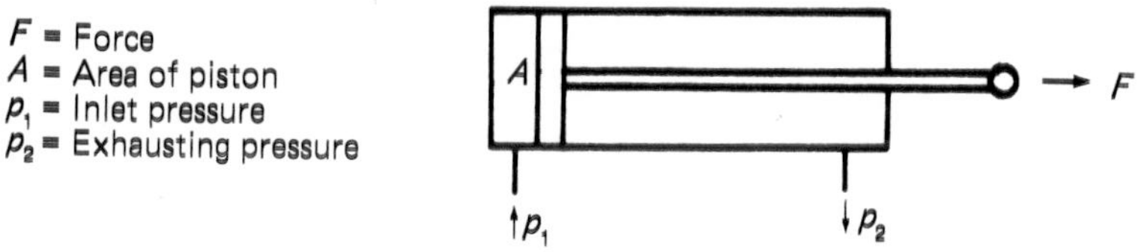

Consider a double-acting cylinder of bore diameter D. The piston area A will be given by:

$$A = \frac{\pi D^2}{4}$$ (since the radius is $\frac{D}{2}$ and the area of a circle is πr^2).

Let the inlet supply air pressure be p_1 and the exhausting air pressure be p_2. These two pressures oppose one another. Therefore the effective pressure producing a force is $p_1 - p_2$.

The force produced by the cylinder is the product of the piston area and the effective pressure acting on the piston. So,

force $F = A(p_1 - p_2)$

but A is $\dfrac{\pi D^2}{4}$

so $F = \dfrac{\pi D^2}{4}(p_1 - p_2)$.

Example

What is the force produced by a double-acting cylinder of 40 mm diameter bore, when the supply air pressure is 0.7 N/mm² and the exhausting air pressure is 0.4 N/mm²?

Using $F = \dfrac{\pi D^2}{4}(p_1 - p_2)$,

$$F = \frac{\pi\, 40 \times 40}{4}(0.7 - 0.4)\ \text{N}$$

$$= \frac{\pi\, 1600}{4} \times 0.3\ \text{N}$$

$$= \pi \times 400 \times 0.3\ \text{N}$$

$$= 377\ \text{N}.$$

Therefore, the force produced by the double-acting cylinder is 377 newtons.

This may not be enough to move a load attached to the cylinder. But, as the exhausting air pressure is continuously falling, the effective pressure producing a force is continually rising. It will eventually reach a value which will enable the load to be moved.

5 Air Bleed and Electrical Control of Circuits

■ **Pressure Sensitive Valves**

Both 3-port and 5-port valves can be obtained with double air pressure operation. To operate, they require air signals at quite a high pressure because of the small surface area of the end of the spool on which the air signals act. A 3-port valve which responds to low pressure air signals is available. It is called a **pressure sensitive valve** (Fig. 5.1).

Fig. 5.1   A diaphragm operated pressure sensitive valve

The valve is operated by a rubber **diaphragm** which has a large surface area (Fig. 5.2). Inside the valve is a piston or spool which is attached to the diaphragm. When a low pressure pilot air signal is applied at the signal port 1 2, the low pressure acting on the large area of the diaphragm produces sufficient force to move the spool. The main supply air at port 1 can now leave the valve from port 2. The pressure sensitive valve is a spring-return valve. When the pilot air signal is removed, the spool returns and allows exhaust air from the cylinder to escape to the atmosphere through exhaust port 3. Since the valve is activated by a diaphragm, it is also called a **diaphragm valve**.

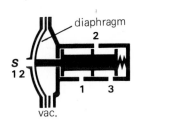

Fig. 5.2   The diaphragm valve

Fig. 5.3
BSI/ISO circuit
diagram symbol
for a pressure
sensitive valve

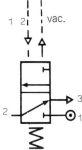

The BSI/ISO symbol for the pressure sensitive valve is shown in Fig. 5.3. This valve can be operated by a pilot air signal with a pressure as low as 0.5 bar. Sometimes pneumatics engineers operate the valve by a vacuum port below the diaphragm. This is why the circuit diagram symbol shows two pilot lines.

1 Is an air signal applied to the pressure sensitive valve by air blown from lungs sufficient to operate it?

■ Air Bleed Circuits

Fig. 5.4   Air bleed circuit –
single-acting cylinder

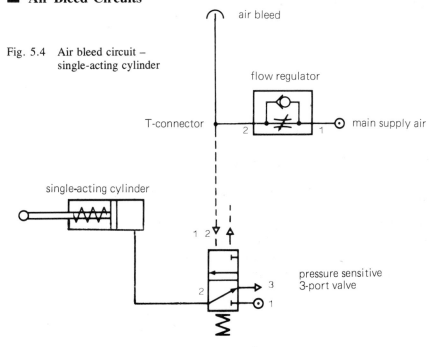

The pressure sensitive valve can be used in air bleed circuits (Fig. 5.4). A flow regulator admits a controlled flow of main air to a pipe with a T-junction. One pipe from this T-connector is left open and bleeds air to the atmosphere. This is why the circuit is called an **air bleed circuit**. When the air bleed is blocked, the pressure in the T-junction pipes increases. This air provides a pilot air signal to port 1 2 of the pressure sensitive valve. When the pressure of this signal reaches about 0.5 bar, the pressure sensitive valve is activated. Main supply air to the valve at port 1 is able to leave from port 2 and make the single-acting cylinder go positive.

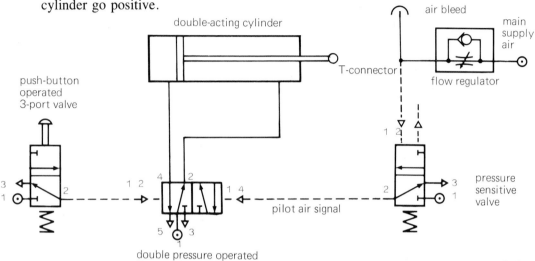

Fig. 5.5   Air bleed circuit – double-acting cylinder

An air bleed circuit can be constructed with a double-acting cylinder (Fig. 5.5). When the air bleed is blocked, the pressure increases in the T-junction pipe which provides the pilot air signal to the pressure sensitive valve. When the signal at port 1 2 reaches about 0.5 bar, the pressure sensitive valve operates. A pilot air signal is then applied to signal port 1 4 of the double pressure operated 5-port valve. Main supply air leaves the 5-port valve at port 4 and the cylinder goes positive. If the air bleed is released, the spring-return removes the output air from port 2 of the pressure sensitive valve. The double pressure operated 5-port valve can then be reset by a pilot air signal from the push-button 3-port valve. The double-acting cylinder will then go negative.

■ Applications for Air Bleed Circuits

Figure 5.6 shows a safety circuit. The press tool operating valve has no main air supply directly available to it. Its supply comes through the pressure sensitive valve which only supplies air to the operating valve when the machine guard is down. When the guard is down it blocks an air bleed, and this causes pressure to build up on the pressure sensitive valve's diaphragm, so turning it 'on'. Only now is air available to operate the press tool.

50

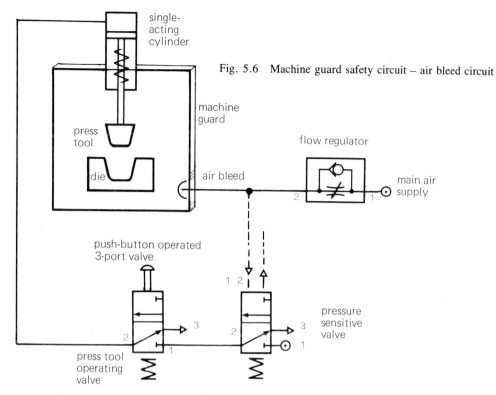

Fig. 5.6   Machine guard safety circuit – air bleed circuit

In a garage with a compressor, a simple method of warning the attendant of a car entering the forecourt is to use an air bleed circuit. A flexible tube is attached to the air bleed pipe. When a car wheel blocks the flexible tube, pressure increases in the T-junction pipes and the pressure sensitive valve is operated. Main air is supplied to a single-acting cylinder which outstrokes and hits a gong (Fig. 5.7).

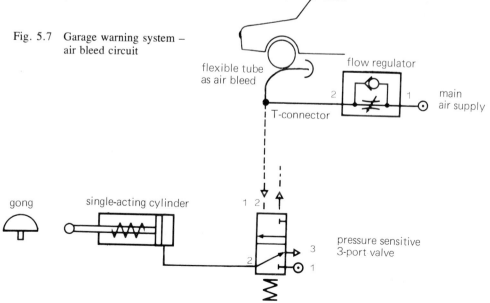

Fig. 5.7   Garage warning system – air bleed circuit

The pressure sensitive valve can be used to make a simple pneumatic combination lock (Fig. 5.8). A door is bolted by the piston rod of a single-acting cylinder. To open the door, four fingers and a thumb have to be placed over the correct combination of five air bleed holes. Five dummy holes, also bleeding air, are included on the combination lock operating panel. Covering the correct holes creates a pilot air signal on the diaphragm of the pressure sensitive valve. Main air flows to the cylinder and the door is unbolted.

Fig. 5.8   Combination door lock – air bleed circuit

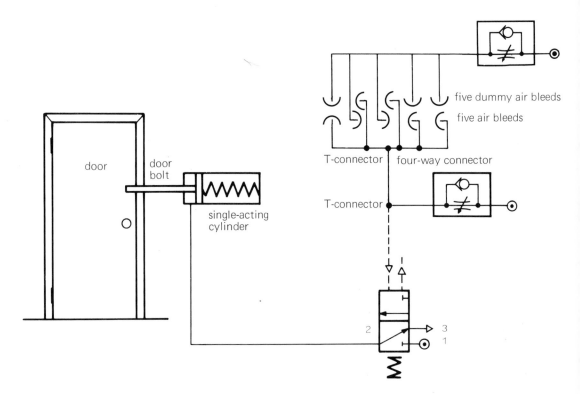

The lock is easily defeated by covering all ten holes at once. To overcome this, the pressure sensitive valve in Fig. 5.8 could be supplied with main air from another pressure sensitive valve. This second valve is controlled by the five dummy air bleeds, and needs to be piped up so that, when all five dummy air bleeds are covered, the main air supply to the valve in Fig. 5.8 is cut off. A clue to how this is done is given in Fig. 5.10. Even with this modification, the system is not totally secure.

  2 What are the weaknesses of the modified lock?

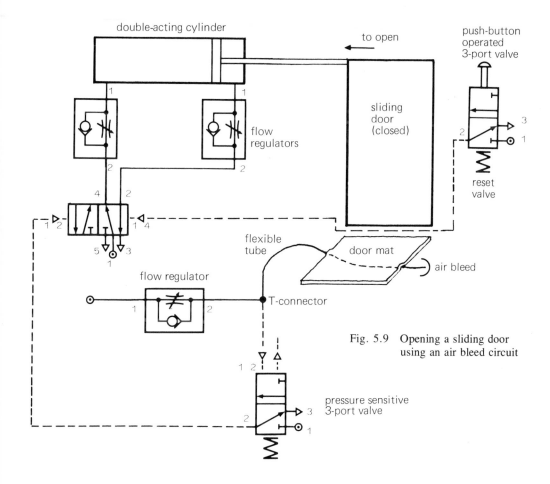

Fig. 5.9 Opening a sliding door using an air bleed circuit

Figure 5.9 shows an air bleed circuit operating a sliding door. Air is bled from a flexible tube beneath the doormat. The air bleed is blocked when a person treads on the mat. This produces an air signal on the pressure sensitive valve. A pilot air signal from the pressure sensitive valve activates the double pressure operated 5-port valve, causing the cylinder to open the sliding door. The door is closed by a reset valve inside the doorway. This system is ideal when traffic through the door is one-way only, but problems arise when traffic is two-way. Consider the problems and how to overcome them.

3 What component controls the piston speed of the double-acting cylinder?

■ Pressure Sensing Circuits

The pressure sensitive valve can be used to detect when a double-acting cylinder is fully outstroked or instroked (Fig. 5.10). It does this by sensing the decay of the exhaust air pressure as the piston reaches the end of its movement.

53

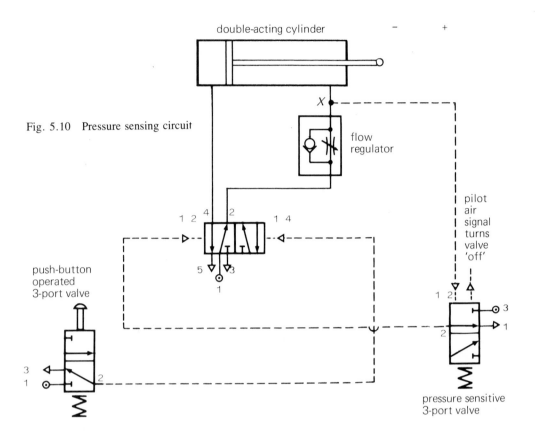

Fig. 5.10   Pressure sensing circuit

double-acting cylinder

flow regulator

pilot air signal turns valve 'off'

push-button operated 3-port valve

pressure sensitive 3-port valve

The pressure sensitive valve has to be piped up in a way different from that previously shown. The main air supply is connected to port 3 (not 1) while port 1 (not 3) becomes the exhaust port. When a pilot air signal is applied at port 1 2, the valve is turned 'off' (instead of 'on'). When the pilot air signal is removed, the valve is turned 'on' (instead of 'off) by the spring-return. Note how the valve's circuit diagram symbol is drawn differently to indicate this new mode of operation.

When the push-button operated 3-port pilot valve is pressed, an air signal goes to port 1 4 of the double pressure operated 5-port valve. This causes the cylinder to go positive. The positive-going piston speed is controlled by a flow regulator in the exhaust part of the circuit. The flow regulator also helps to maintain an air pressure at X (Fig. 5.10) until the end of the outstroke, when the exhaust pressure at X falls. The pressure of the pilot air signal, held on port 1 2 of the pressure sensitive valve, falls below 0.5 bar. The valve was 'off', but now the spring-return turns the valve 'on'. Main supply air flows to signal port 1 2 of the double pressure operated 5-port valve. The cylinder goes negative. This instroke movement occurs automatically when the diaphragm valve senses the exhaust air pressure decay at X at the end of the outstroke.

■ Solenoid Valves

An electrical circuit may be used to control a pneumatic circuit. This is made possible by an electro-pneumatic valve such as a solenoid valve. A **solenoid valve** can be a 3-port or 5-port valve. The **solenoid** consists of a coil of wire. When an electric current is passed through a wire **coil**, it produces a magnetic field around the coil. If an iron armature is placed in the energised coil, it is attracted into the coil. This movement of an iron armature is used to operate the valve. Figure 5.11 shows an example of a solenoid operated 3-port valve. Figure 5.12 shows its BSI/ISO symbol.

Fig. 5.11   A solenoid operated 3-port valve

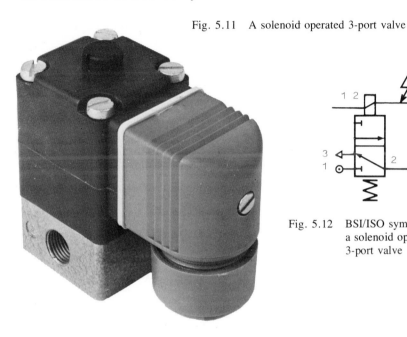

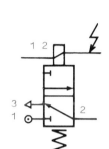

Fig. 5.12   BSI/ISO symbol for a solenoid operated 3-port valve

Figure 5.13 shows a section through a solenoid operated 3-port valve. Main supply air is connected to the inlet port 1. With no electric current flowing in the coil, the main supply air is prevented from passing through the valve by a spring-loaded ferrous metal armature. (A ferrous metal contains iron.) When the solenoid coil is energised by an electric current, the armature is attracted towards the centre of the coil. This allows the main supply air to flow from port 2.

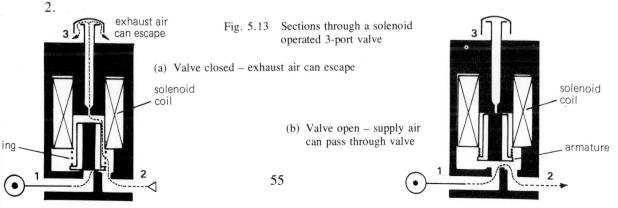

Fig. 5.13   Sections through a solenoid operated 3-port valve

(a) Valve closed – exhaust air can escape

(b) Valve open – supply air can pass through valve

exhaust air can escape

solenoid coil

solenoid coil

ing

armature

55

■ Using the Solenoid Valve

The advantages of using solenoid valves are:

(a) electrical signals can be transmitted over much greater distances than pneumatic signals;

(b) electrical signals respond faster than pneumatic signals;

(c) less energy is used with electrical control signals than pneumatic signals (compressed air is expensive to use for control signals);

(d) electrical and electronic signals are more efficient than pneumatic signals;

(e) the components used in electrical and electronic control circuits are cheaper and use less space than pneumatic components.

Solenoid valve coils can be obtained with different working voltages. For example:

  12 volt dc
  24 volt dc
  50 volt dc
110 volt ac
240 volt ac (common electrical mains voltage)
440 volt ac.

For safety reasons, low voltage solenoid valves should be used. The solenoid valves in the Pneumatics kit operate on 12 volts dc.

The solenoid valve can be used to control a single-acting cylinder (Fig. 5.14).

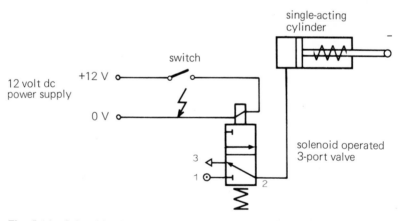

Fig. 5.14   Solenoid valve control of a single-acting cylinder

The symbol ⟋ is used to indicate the electrical wires from the solenoid valve to the power supply. When the switch is closed, the solenoid coil is energised and main supply air flows from port 2 of the valve. The single-acting cylinder goes positive. The fast response of the solenoid valve is advantageous in controlling cylinders from a remote position.

56

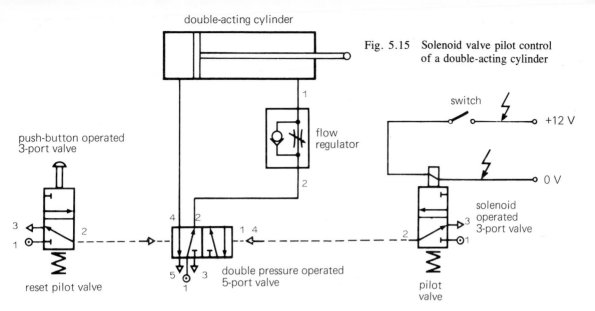

Fig. 5.15 Solenoid valve pilot control of a double-acting cylinder

The solenoid valve can be used as a pilot valve to control a double-acting cylinder (Fig. 5.15). When the switch is closed, a pilot air signal is released by the solenoid valve. This air signal operates the control valve, and the double-acting cylinder goes positive.

4 How can the cylinder be reset to a negative position?
5 In which direction is the piston speed controlled?

In industrial chemical plants, the valves in pipes that carry dangerous fluids are often opened or shut by a pneumatic cylinder controlled from a remote position. The solenoid valve circuit in Fig. 5.15 is suitable for this application.

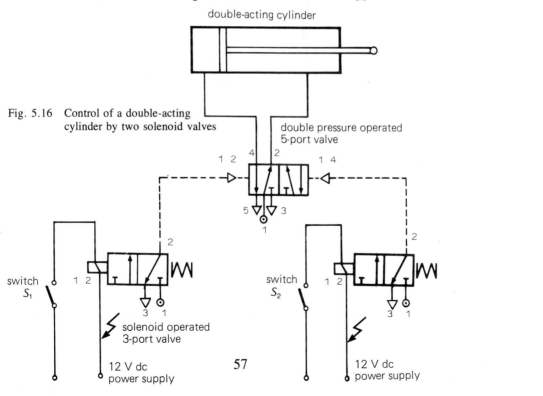

Fig. 5.16 Control of a double-acting cylinder by two solenoid valves

Figure 5.16 shows how two solenoid valves can be used as pilot valves to control a double-acting cylinder. When the electrical switch S_2 is closed, the cylinder goes positive. When switch S_2 is opened and switch S_1 closed, the cylinder goes negative.

6 Why is it not possible to make the cylinder go negative while switch S_2 is closed?

The use of two separate switches is not convenient and can cause signalling problems at the 5-port valve. One method of overcoming this problem is to use a single-pole double-throw electrical switch to operate both solenoid valves alternately (Fig. 5.17).

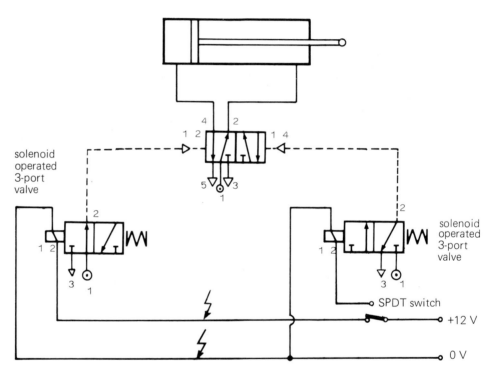

Fig. 5.17 Operating two solenoid valves by a single-pole double-throw electrical switch

■ The Pneumatic Counter

The **pneumatic counter** counts air signals. The number of air signals is recorded on a five-digit display panel, and the counter can be reset to zero by a manual reset push-button. Figure 5.18 shows a pneumatic counter. Figure 5.19 shows its BSI/ISO symbol. The pneumatic counter is similar to an electrical counter but, unlike an electrical counter, it is safe to use in dangerous environments such as petro-chemical plants or in the explosives industry.

58

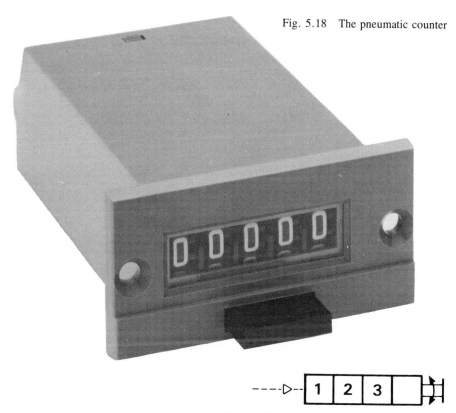

Fig. 5.18   The pneumatic counter

Fig. 5.19   The BSI/ISO symbol for a pneumatic counter

The pneumatic counter can be used with an air bleed circuit (Fig. 5.20). Whenever the air bleed is blocked and released, a signal is recorded on the display panel. When the air bleed is released, the air which signalled the counter exhausts to atmosphere through the pressure sensitive valve.

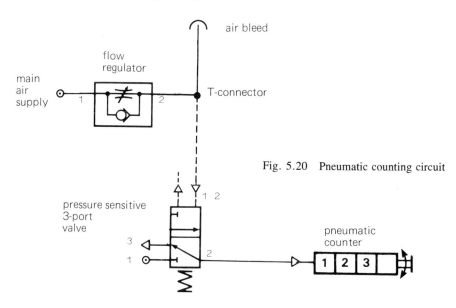

Fig. 5.20   Pneumatic counting circuit

This circuit could be used to count objects passing the air bleed. For example, if a flexible tube is attached to the air bleed, then every time the tube is squeezed and released, the counter records one impulse. The counting circuit could be used to count cars passing along a road (Fig. 5.21).

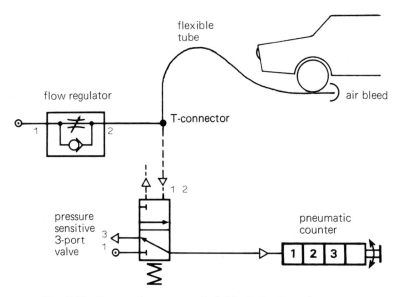

Fig. 5.21   Pneumatic counter and air bleed circuit used to count cars

7 Assuming only cars passed along the road, would the number on the counter be the number of cars which had gone by?

Answers to Questions
1 No. An air signal pressure of 0.5 bar cannot be produced by the lungs.
2 Burglars, locksmiths and security firms do not give away their secrets! Develop and test your own ideas for making the lock fully secure.
3 The flow regulator.
4 By pressing the button operated 3-port pilot valve.
5 On the outstroke.
6 Because the double pressure operated 5-port valve cannot be signalled from both sides at the same time.
7 No. The front and back wheels operate the counter. The number of cars is half the number on the counter. In all counting circuits, special care is necessary to ensure that the figures obtained are the figures required.

6 Time Delays

■ The Reservoir

It is often necessary to produce a time delay in the operation of a pneumatic circuit. For example, a pneumatically operated machine may have to perform a sequence of operations, one after another. When one operation has finished, it may be essential to delay the start of the next operation for a few seconds or even minutes. Such a time delay is achieved by use of a **reservoir**. A reservoir is an empty cylindrical vessel. An air reservoir is shown in Fig. 6.1

Fig. 6.1   An air reservoir

A reservoir resembles a double-acting cylinder without a piston and piston rod. It is made from a cylinder body, cast end caps and four tie bars. Any strong pressure vessel could act as a reservoir. A long length of nylon tube can be coiled and used as one. The BSI/ISO symbol for a reservoir is shown in Fig. 6.2.

Fig. 6.2   BSI/ISO symbol for a reservoir

61

■ Time Delay in Pneumatic Circuits

In all pneumatic circuits, there is a short time delay between a signal being given and the start of the required piston movement. This **time delay** occurs because it takes time for air to flow into and raise the pressure in the pilot pipe lines between the pilot valve and the double pressure operated control valve. The longer the pilot lines, the longer the time delay.

If a reservoir is placed in the pilot pipe line, the line volume is greatly increased and time delays of several seconds are possible. The larger the reservoir volume, the longer the time delay. Reservoirs are usually used with a flow regulator. These control the rate of flow of air into the reservoir and hence the rate of pressure increase in the reservoir. This control makes possible longer time delays. Figure 6.3 shows a typical time delay circuit.

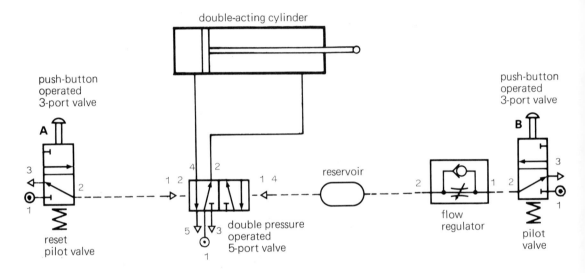

Fig. 6.3   Pilot valve control of double-acting cylinder with time delay

When pilot valve *B* is pressed, the pilot air signal from port 2 is controlled by the flow regulator. Air flows slowly into the reservoir. It takes several seconds for the air pressure in the reservoir to increase sufficiently to operate the double pressure operated 5-port valve at signal port 1 4. The cylinder then goes positive. Pilot valve *B* has to be held in the 'operate' position for the period of the time delay in order to signal the cylinder to go positive. When pilot valve *B* is released, the air stored in the reservoir exhausts to atmosphere. It does this by flowing through the 'free flow' route of the flow regulator to pilot valve *B* and out through port 3. The cylinder is made to instroke by pressing reset pilot valve *A*.

Fig. 6.4   Pneumatic time delay circuit

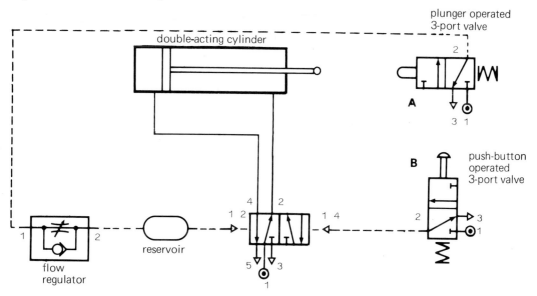

A reservoir can be used to return a piston rod after a time delay of several
seconds (Fig. 6.4). When the push-button operated 3-port pilot valve is pressed,
an air signal at signal port 1 4 of the double pressure operated 5-port valve
causes the cylinder to go positive. At the end of its outstroke, the piston rod
trips a plunger operated 3-port pilot valve. This produces an air signal which is
controlled by a flow regulator. The reservoir slowly fills with air. After a time
delay of a few seconds, the pressure in the reservoir rises to a level sufficient to
operate the double pressure operated 5-port valve. The piston rod goes negative.

■ Time Delay Circuit Applications

A time delay circuit in which a piston rod is held positive for a few seconds is
useful in clamping applications where impact adhesives are being used
(Fig. 6.5). When the push-button operated pilot valve is pressed, the cylinder,
with its pressure pad, goes positive. The veneer (thin sheet wood or plastic) is
clamped for a few seconds because the start of the piston instroke is delayed.
This allows the impact adhesive time to grip. The air signal from a roller-trip
valve causes the cylinder to return after a short time delay.

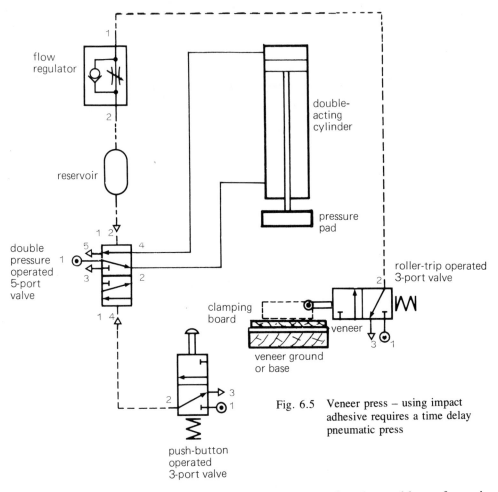

Fig. 6.5 Veneer press – using impact
adhesive requires a time delay
pneumatic press

A pneumatic time delay circuit could be used to solve the problem of opening
and closing a car park barrier. The barrier must lift as the car approaches it and
fall after the car has passed through. A pneumatic solution might have a roller-
trip valve to open the car park barrier, and a time delay circuit to close the
barrier. A block diagram of the solution is shown in Fig. 6.6

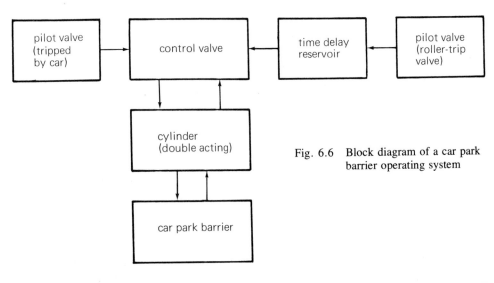

Fig. 6.6 Block diagram of a car park
barrier operating system

Figure 6.7 shows the pneumatic circuit and a schematic layout of the components of the car park barrier. When a car wheel rolls over roller-trip operated 3-port valve *A*, an air signal to port 1 4 of the control valve causes the cylinder to go positive. The car park barrier is opened. When valve *B* is tripped by the end of the barrier arm, an air signal is sent through the flow regulator and reservoir to signal port 1 2 of the control valve. After a pre-determined time delay, the car park barrier closes.

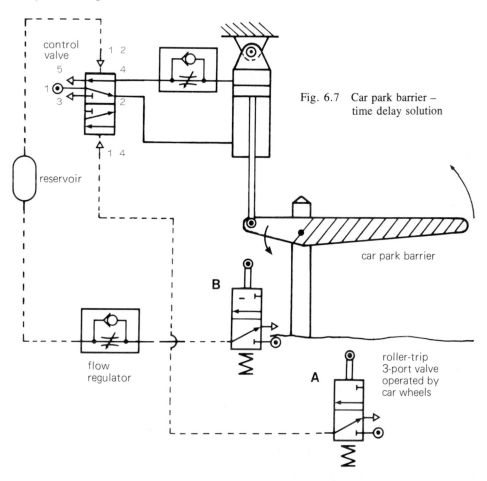

Fig. 6.7   Car park barrier –
time delay solution

1 Can you see any snags that might arise in the operation of this car park barrier?

■ A More Complex Time Delay Circuit

In Figs. 6.5 and 6.7, the time delay circuit which sent the piston negative after several seconds was fed with air from a roller-trip valve. It is possible to dispense with this 3-port valve and still have a system which works in the same way. Figure 6.8*a* shows the basic circuit diagram.

g. 6.8   A time delay piston return circuit

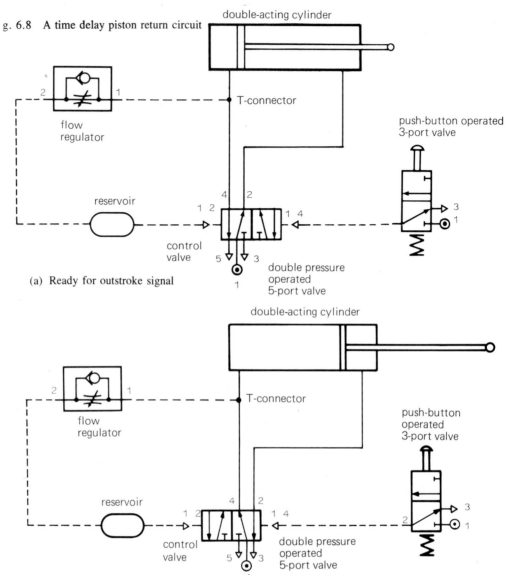

double-acting cylinder

2 ⟋ 1
flow
regulator

reservoir

control
valve

4 2
1 2 · 1 4
5 ▽ ▽ 3

T-connector

push-button operated
3-port valve

3
1

double pressure
operated
5-port valve
1

(a) Ready for outstroke signal

double-acting cylinder

2 ⟋ 1
flow
regulator

reservoir

control
valve

4 2
1 2 · 1 4
5 ▽ ▽ 3

T-connector

push-button
operated
3-port valve

3
2 · 1

double pressure
operated
5-port valve
1

(b) Automatic instroke about to be signalled

When the push-button operated 3-port valve is pressed and released, the main
supply air is connected to the cylinder by a pipe from port 4 of the control
valve. The piston goes positive (Fig. 6.8b). A T-connector in the pipe from port
4 routes an air pilot signal through a flow regulator and reservoir to the control
valve. The reservoir slowly fills with air. When the pressure of the air in the
reservoir reaches a certain value, its signal on port 1 2 of the control valve
makes the valve change position. The cylinder goes negative. The reservoir
discharges through the free flow route of the flow regulator and port 5 of the
control valve (Fig. 6.8a). The flow regulator needs careful setting for reliable
operation of the circuit.

66

☐ Reservoir Volume

The time delay that can be achieved in a circuit is determined by the **reservoir volume** and the rate at which the reservoir air pressure is allowed to rise. A flow regulator is used to control the rate at which this is allowed to rise. The time delay obtainable from any given reservoir can be altered by adjusting the flow regulator. The table shows the range of time delay obtainable with the Martonair reservoirs in the Pneumatics kit.

Reservoir Type	Capacity (cm³)	Minimum Delay	Maximum Delay
M/810/13	130	2 sec	16 sec
M/810/25	250	4 sec	32 sec

☐ Comparison of Systems

A pneumatic reservoir can be compared with an electronic capacitor. It takes time for air pressure to rise in a reservoir, and it takes time for a capacitor to store up electric charge. This time factor allows both devices to be used in time delay circuits. Figure 6.9 shows a pneumatic time delay circuit and an electronic time delay circuit.

In the pneumatic circuit, when 3-port valve B is pressed and held, the cylinder goes positive after a short time delay caused by the reservoir and flow regulator.

Fig. 6.9   Comparison of pneumatic and electronic time delay circuits

(a) Pneumatic time delay circuit

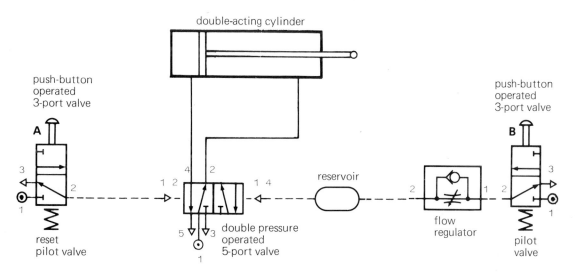

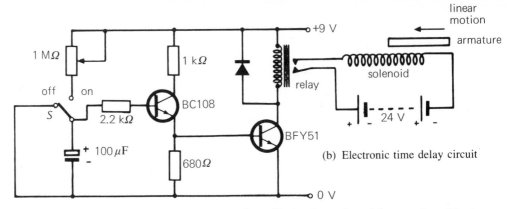

(b) Electronic time delay circuit

In the electronic circuit, the pneumatic cylinder is replaced by a solenoid. A solenoid is an electrical device for producing linear motion. It consists of a coil of wire wound on a hollow bobbin. An iron armature is free to move into the centre of the solenoid. When an electric current flows through the coil of wire, a magnetic field is generated. The magnetic field causes the armature to move into the centre of the solenoid. In Fig. 6.9b, when switch S is turned to the 'on' position, the capacitor charges up. After a short time delay, the transistors are turned 'on'. The transistors control a relay. The relay contacts close. The solenoid is energised and the armature moves into the solenoid with linear motion.

■ Using a Reservoir with a Single-acting Cylinder

A reservoir and flow regulator can be used to create a time delay in a single-acting cylinder circuit (Fig. 6.10).

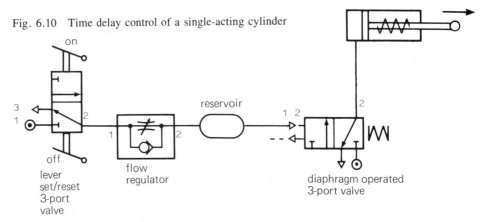

Fig. 6.10   Time delay control of a single-acting cylinder

When the lever set/reset 3-port valve is turned 'on', main supply air passes through a flow regulator and into a reservoir. The supply air flow is controlled by the flow regulator. After a short time delay, the pressure of the air in the reservoir is high enough to operate the diaphragm of the pressure sensitive valve. Main supply air passes through the pressure sensitive valve and the single-acting cylinder goes positive. Figure 6.11 shows a lever set/reset 3-port valve and its BSI/ISO symbol.

68

Fig. 6.11　(a) Lever set/reset 3-port valve

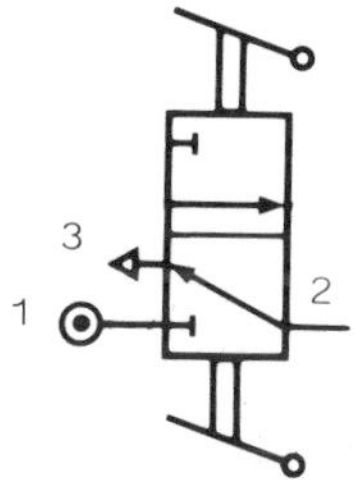

(b) BSI/ISO symbol for lever
set/reset 3-port valve

☐ **Pulse Circuit**

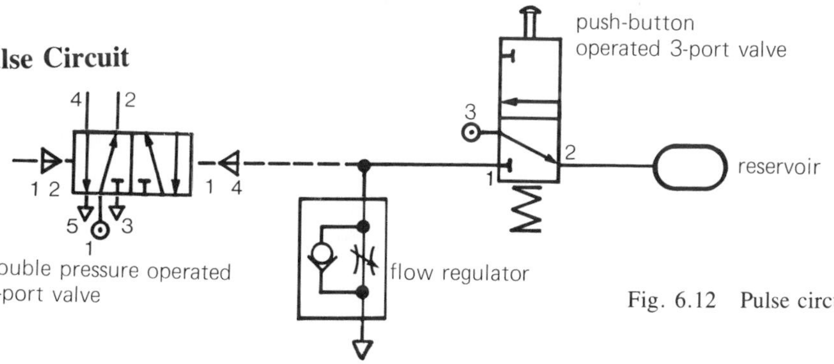

push-button
operated 3-port valve

reservoir

double pressure operated
5-port valve

flow regulator

Fig. 6.12　Pulse circuit

The circuit in Fig. 6.12 is unusual because the main air supply is connected to port 3 of the pilot valve and not port 1. Note that this mode of connection is only possible with spool valves and not poppet valves. The only 3-port spool valves in the basic Pneumatics kit are the diaphragm operated valves.

The reservoir is used to store energy for producing a pilot signal rather than as a time delay device. When the push-button valve is operated, air in the reservoir discharges from port 1 and signals signal port 1 4 of the double pressure operated 5-port valve. A flow regulator allows the air discharged from the reservoir to bleed away to the atmosphere. In this way, the signal at port 1 4 of the 5-port valve is automatically removed even though the push-button is still held down. Thus the 5-port valve can respond to a signal at signal port 1 2.

This pulse circuit is very useful in situations where a pilot valve is likely to be held 'on', and yet only a momentary signal is required. It avoids the problem of conflicting signals on a double pressure operated 5-port valve. This is important in sequential control circuits (Chapter 9).

Answer to Question
The barrier will descend on a stalled car. How can this be overcome?

7 Automatic Circuits

■ **Semi-automatic Control**

Pilot valve control of a double-acting cylinder has formed the basis of much of the work in this course. The basic circuit shown in Fig. 7.1 can be modified by the use of different kinds of pilot valve. The pilot valves signal a control valve which operates the cylinder. The control valve is a double pressure operated 5-port valve.

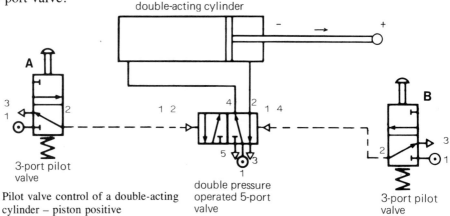

Fig. 7.1   Pilot valve control of a double-acting cylinder – piston positive

1 In the circuit diagram shown in Fig. 7.1, which pilot valve must be pressed to make the cylinder go negative?

If pilot valve *A* in Fig. 7.1 is replaced by a plunger or roller-trip operated 3-port valve, an automatic piston return circuit is achieved (Fig. 7.2). If pilot valve *B* is pressed, the cylinder goes positive. When the piston rod strikes the plunger or roller-trip of pilot valve *A*, an air signal is sent to signal port 1 2 of the control valve. The piston is automatically returned. This is a **semi-automatic circuit**.

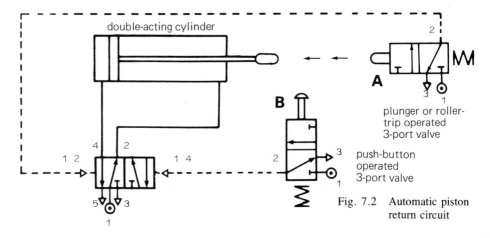

Fig. 7.2   Automatic piston return circuit

A more complex automatic piston return circuit is shown in Fig. 7.3.

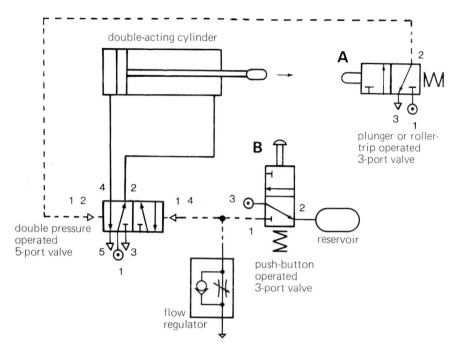

Fig. 7.3   Alternative automatic piston return circuit

This circuit uses the pulse circuit described at the end of Chapter 6. With pilot valve *B* in its unoperated position, the main supply air is connected to a reservoir. When pilot valve *B* is pressed, the air in the reservoir discharges into the pilot line. A pilot air signal operates the control valve at signal port 1 4, and the cylinder goes positive. The pilot air signal bleeds to atmosphere through the flow regulator fitted in the pilot line. This allows the control valve spool to be re-signalled when the piston rod hits the plunger operated valve *A*, even though push-button *B* is still held down. The circuit provides **semi-automatic control** of the cylinder.

Semi-automatic control can be achieved by the use of a flow regulator and reservoir (see Fig. 6.8). This circuit was described in the last chapter. The piston is made to outstroke by operating the push-button 3-port valve. The piston instrokes automatically. By careful adjustment of the flow regulator, the time delay between the end of the outstroke and the start of the instroke can be removed. Another semi-automatic circuit was described in Chapter 5, page 54. Re-read this section now.

In all of the semi-automatic circuits, the pistons can be made to automatically outstroke, rather than instroke, by rearranging the components and the pipework.

■ Automatic Control

Fully **automatic circuits** operate continuously without manual intervention. When the main supply air is turned on, an automatic control system produces reciprocation of the piston in the cylinder.

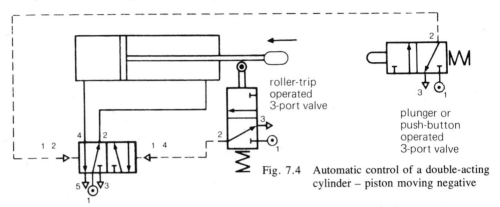

roller-trip operated 3-port valve

plunger or push-button operated 3-port valve

Fig. 7.4   Automatic control of a double-acting cylinder – piston moving negative

Figure 7.4 shows an automatic circuit. Once the main supply air is connected to the control and pilot valves, the cylinder reciprocates backwards and forwards. This is an example of **automatic control** of a cylinder. The same type of control is achieved by the use of two roller-trip 3-port valves as pilot valves (Fig. 7.5).

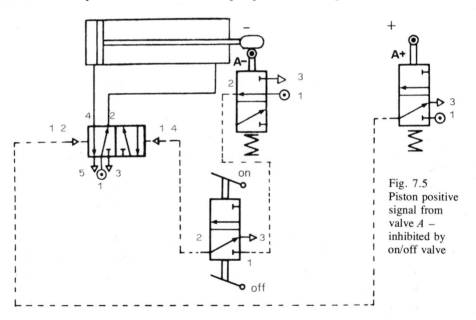

Fig. 7.5
Piston positive signal from valve *A* – inhibited by on/off valve

The automatic cycle can be interrupted instroke by putting a lever set/reset 3-port valve in one pilot line to act as an on/off switch (Fig. 7.5).

   2 Could a push-button operated (spring-return) 3-port valve be used to stop and start the automatic cycle of the circuit shown in Fig. 7.5?

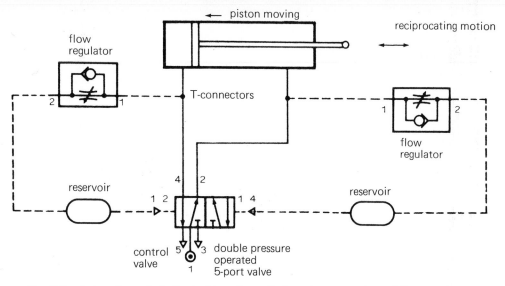

Fig. 7.6   Automatic control of a double-acting cylinder using reservoirs and flow regulators

The time delay created by a reservoir and flow regulator can be used to achieve automatic control of a double-acting cylinder (Fig. 7.6). This circuit produces an automatic cycle with the cylinder reciprocating backwards and forwards. At the end of each piston movement, the reservoir which signalled that movement discharges through the free flow route of its flow regulator to one of the exhaust ports of the control valve. The cycle can be interrupted instroke by placing a lever set/reset 3-port valve in the pilot line between the reservoir and signal port 1 4 of the control valve (Fig. 7.7).

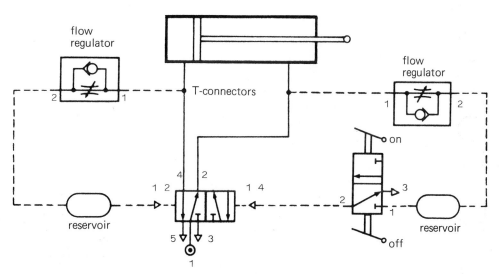

Fig. 7.7   Interrupting the automatic cycle – piston positive signal inhibited

The flow regulators require careful adjustment to ensure reliable operation of the circuit. If required, a limited time delay at the end of each or either piston stroke can be obtained by adjustment of the flow regulators.

73

☐ Comparison of Systems

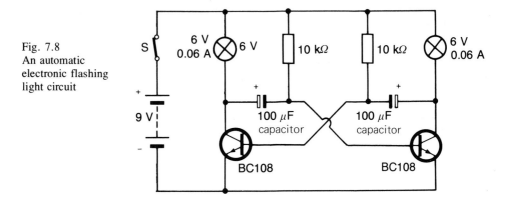

Fig. 7.8
An automatic
electronic flashing
light circuit

Figure 7.8 is an electronic circuit equivalent to the pneumatic reciprocating piston circuit shown in Fig. 7.7. Both circuits require components whose properties are related to time: a reservoir and a capacitor. In these circuits, two of each component are required. When the pneumatic circuit is switched on, the piston reciprocates positive and negative continuously. When the electronic circuit is switched on the lights alternately and continuously flash on and off.

■ Alternative Automatic Circuits

Pressure sensitive valves, used as described in Chapter 5, sense when the piston of a cylinder is fully positive or fully negative (Fig. 7.9).

Fig. 7.9   Using pressure sensitive valves to produce automatic control

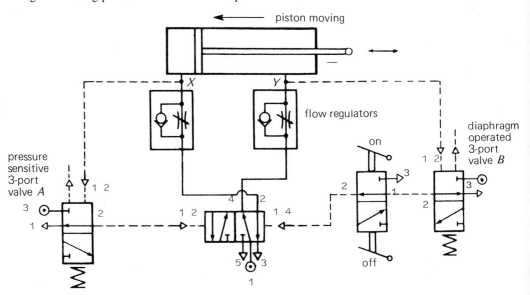

The pressure sensitive valves have main air connected to port 3 and not port 1. With this arrangement, a signal at port 1 2 holds the valve 'off'. When the signal at port 1 2 is removed, the spring-return turns the valve 'on' and allows main air to flow in at port 3 and out at port 2.

The piston in Fig. 7.9 is just completing an instroke. When the pressure of the exhausting air at X decays, an air signal will be removed from port 1 2 of valve A. The spring-return will allow main air to flow through valve A to signal port 1 2 of the 5-port valve. The piston will go positive. Valve B will sense the decay of the exhaust air pressure at Y and will signal the piston negative. The cycle is stopped outstroke by the on/off lever set/reset valve.

Automatic control of a cylinder can also be achieved electrically (Fig. 7.10). Microswitches are used instead of roller-trip valves and are operated by the piston rod. The microswitches control solenoid valves.

Fig. 7.10   Solenoid valves and microswitches used to produce an automatic control circuit

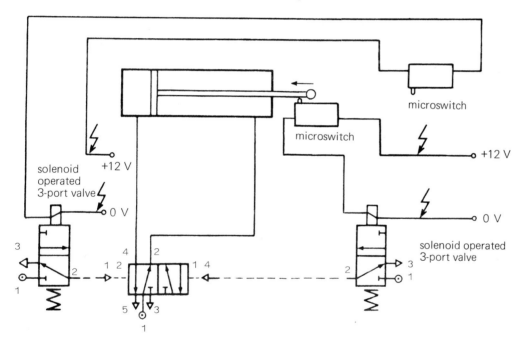

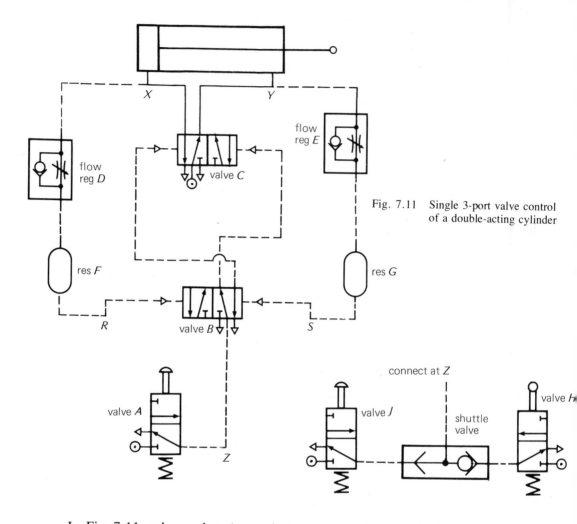

Fig. 7.11 Single 3-port valve control of a double-acting cylinder

In Fig. 7.11, when valve A was last pressed and released, four things happened.

1 The air signal from valve A passed through the left-hand flow pattern of valve B and set up the left-hand flow pattern of valve C.

2 The result was that the main supply air entered the cylinder and moved the piston negative.

3 At the same time the main supply air was routed through the T-connector at Y to flow regulator E and reservoir G, and set up the right-hand flow pattern of valve B.

4 This enables the next signal from valve A to set up the right-hand flow pattern of valve C. This will send the piston positive.

The circuit shown in Fig. 7.11 can be made to operate in three different ways.

1 When valve A is pressed and released immediately, the piston goes positive. When valve A is pressed and released again, the piston goes negative. If valve A is held 'on', the cylinder will reciprocate. To ensure only one cylinder

movement per valve operation, valve A could be used to form the pulse circuit described at the end of Chapter 6.

2 If valve A is removed and main air supplied at Z, the piston reciprocates continuously and automatically. The reciprocation can be stopped instroke or outstroke by a lever set/reset 3-port valve placed at R or S.

3 A shuttle valve can be connected at Z. Valves H and J are connected to the shuttle valve. Valve H is placed so that it is operated by the piston rod at the end of its outstroke. When valve J is pressed and released, the piston goes positive. Valve H is operated by the piston rod. The piston goes negative and stops. The circuit operates semi-automatically. Valve H can also be placed so that the piston rod operates it at the end of its instroke.

When first connected, the circuit must always be adjusted for correct non-automatic operation as follows. Valve A is pressed and held 'on'. The piston reciprocates. Flow regulators D and E are adjusted so that the piston rod moves its full stroke and stops momentarily before moving again.

When the circuit is required to reciprocate automatically, the start of an automatic movement can be delayed by closing the appropriate flow regulator. This circuit performs more reliably than the circuit shown in Fig. 7.6.

■ Automatic Circuit Applications

Automatic control circuits can be used for applications that require a reciprocating movement. Examples are hacksawing, filing, riveting, sanding and polishing machines. Figures 7.12 to 7.14 show further applications of automatic control circuits. Study the applications carefully and think about how the circuits work.

Fig. 7.12 Pneumatic polishing machine

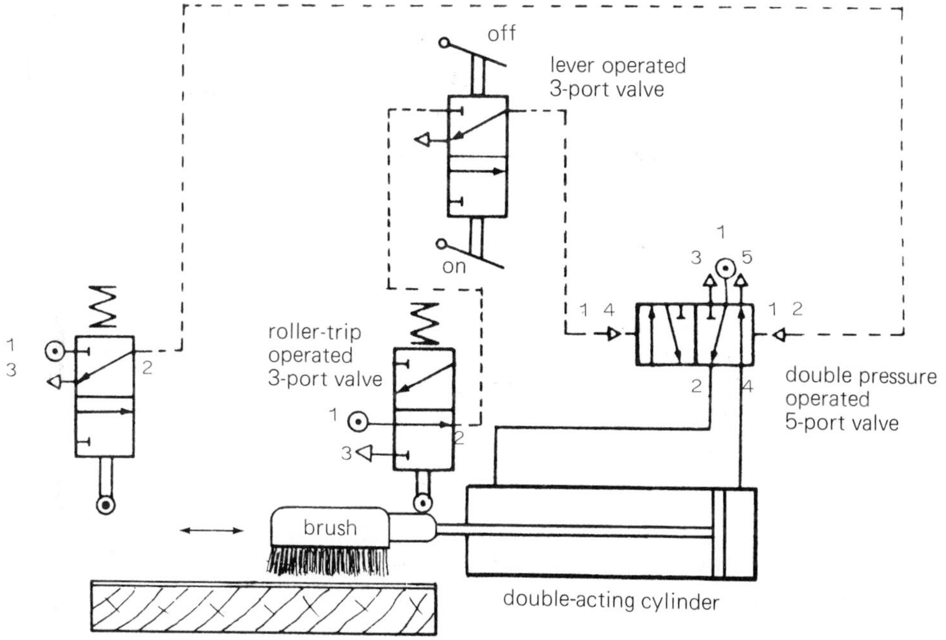

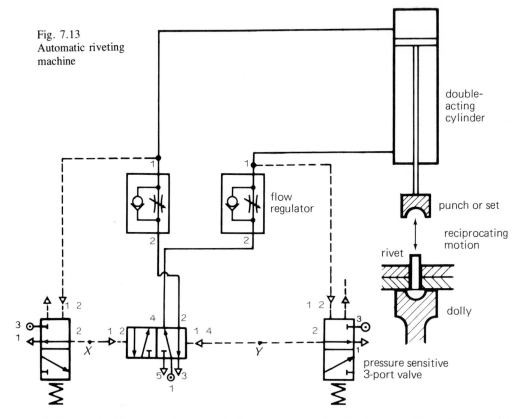

Fig. 7.13
Automatic riveting
machine

3 *Figure 7.13 shows the circuit for an automatic riveting machine. To stop the piston instroke, where should a lever set/reset 3-port valve be placed, at X or Y?*

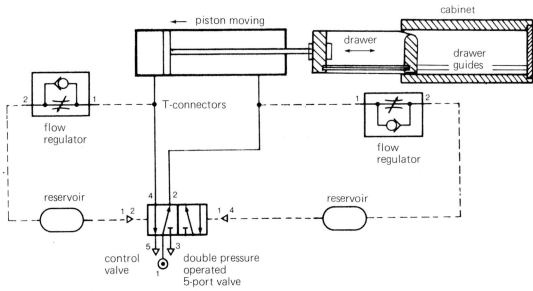

Fig. 7.14   Pneumatic test rig to examine the wear properties of drawer guides

Figure 7.14 shows a testing machine to examine the wear properties of drawer guides in a wooden cabinet. The drawer is reciprocated in and out of the cabinet many times, and the extent of the wear on the drawer and guides is checked at regular intervals. Drawer guides made of different materials can be tested by this pneumatic test rig.

■ Mechanisation

Manual work is when a job has to be done by human labour with few, if any, tools and aids. For example, if a load of sand was delivered to your house, and it was dumped in the road, you would have to do manual work to move the sand from the road to the back garden. In order to move the sand quickly, you could use tools and simple machines. You could use a shovel to lift the sand and a wheelbarrow to move the sand into the garden.

When work has to be done, we are usually interested in ways of doing it quickly and with the least effort. This often means using a machine to do the work. Replacing human or animal work by machinery is called **mechanisation**. Consider the situation shown in Fig. 7.15a. The problem is to move heavy paving slabs from one building to another. There are a number of solutions to the problem. Each involves a greater or lesser degree of mechanisation.

Fig. 7.15 Solutions to the problem of moving paving slabs

(continued overleaf)

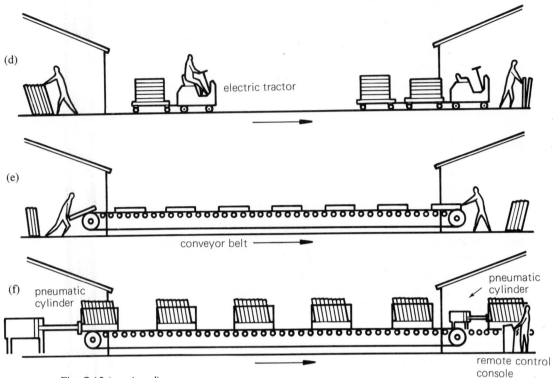

(d) electric tractor

(e) conveyor belt →

(f) pneumatic cylinder   pneumatic cylinder

remote control console

Fig. 7.15 (*continued*)

Solution (*a*) Pick up the heavy paving slab and carry it across the yard to the second building. This is hard work, frequent rests are needed and it takes a long time.

Solution (*b*) Use a two-wheeled trolley. The heavy slabs do not need to be carried, but the trolley has to be loaded and unloaded. The whole operation still takes a long time, but the work is easier.

Solution (*c*) Use a four-wheeled truck to move several slabs at one time. This is still hard work, but the job is completed more quickly. The slabs still need to be loaded and unloaded manually.

Solution (*d*) Use an electric or petrol-engined tractor to pull several four-wheeled trucks. This only reduces the time and effort expended on moving the slabs.

Solution (*e*) Install a conveyor belt between the two buildings. The conveyor belt provides quick, continuous movement of paving slabs. One man is required to load the conveyor belt and another to unload it.

Solution (*f*) Install pneumatic cylinders to load and unload the conveyor belt. If the paving slabs are moved in containers rather than individually, time is saved. The complete system can be controlled from a remote position by one man at a control console. Many slabs are now moved quickly with a minimum of human effort.

80

One factory's solution to the problem of moving paving slabs is shown in Fig. 7.16a–d. Study the pictures carefully, noting the various pneumatic cylinders.

Fig. 7.16   (a) Slabs about to be loaded on a truck   (b) Paving slabs loaded on a truck

(c) Truck moves slabs towards conveyor rollers   (d) Slabs about to be off-loaded on to the conveyor rollers

In the system illustrated in Fig. 7.16, each of the pneumatic cylinders has to operate at the right moment in the sequence of movements. To achieve this, a **sequential control** system is required. This is the subject of the next chapter.

Answers to Questions
1 Pilot valve A.
2 Yes, but the button will have to be kept pressed to operate the automatic cycle. The cycle will stop if the button is released.
3 The lever set/reset valve is placed at X.

8 Sequential Control

■ **The Need for Sequential Control**

When several pneumatic cylinders have to operate in a pre-determined order called a 'sequence', a **sequential control** system is required. Sequential control is used in many industrial applications. Figures 1.3, 1.4, 1.5 and 7.16 all show applications of pneumatics where cylinders must move in the correct sequence.

Figure 8.1 shows pneumatics applied to a double plastic pressing operation. Cylinders A and B operate two pressing dies that are used to shape a sheet of hot plastic. The plastic sheet is clamped over a wooden former with two dish-shaped recesses. The cylinders then operate in a pre-determined sequence.

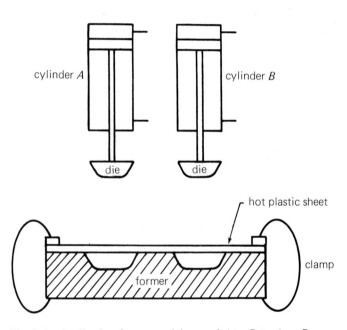

Fig. 8.1   Application for sequential control $A+$, $B+$, $A-$, $B-$

Figure 8.2 shows each stage in the sequence of movements. The operator gives the 'start' signal. Cylinder A presses the first dish shape and then cylinder B presses the second shape. Cylinder A releases the first die, and then cylinder B releases the second die. The sequence then stops. The formed plastic is removed and new hot plastic is placed over the former. The operator then restarts the sequence.

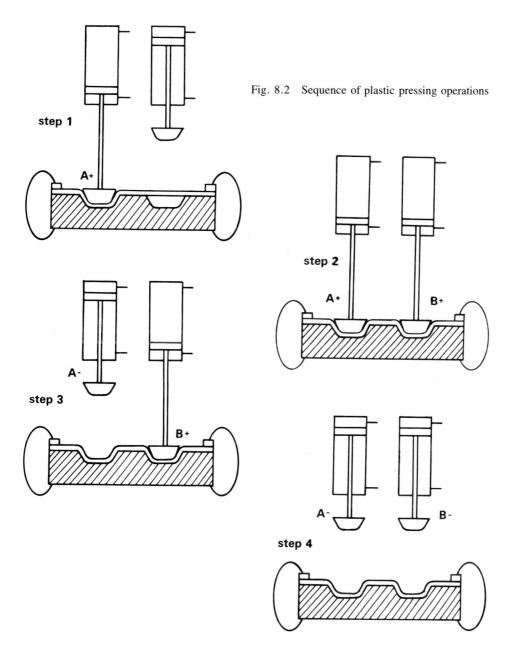

Fig. 8.2   Sequence of plastic pressing operations

The sequence of movements can be set out simply as:

    start,
    cylinder $A+$,
    cylinder $B+$,
    cylinder $A-$,
    cylinder $B-$,
    stop.

■ Achieving Sequential Control

Figure 8.3 shows a basic semi-automatic circuit. When the push-button valve is pressed and released, the piston outstrokes. At the end of the outstroke the piston rod operates the roller-trip valve. The resulting signal from this valve causes the piston to instroke and stop.

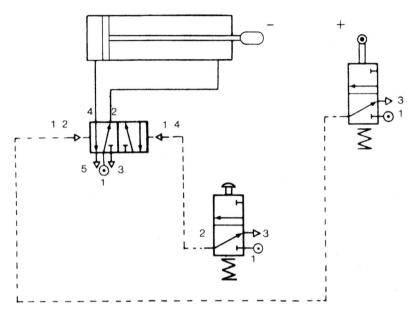

Fig. 8.3   Semi-automatic circuit – automatic piston return

Control of the sequence:

start, cylinder $A+$, cylinder $B+$, cylinder $A-$, cylinder $B-$, stop; is achieved by a simple extension of the basic circuit shown in Fig. 8.3. The circuit can be drawn and understood by going through the sequence step by step and seeing how each movement triggers the next.

Fig. 8.4   The two cylinders A and B with control valves

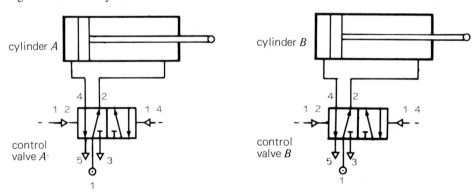

Figure 8.4 shows the two cylinders *A* and *B*. Each cylinder has a double pressure operated 5-port valve to act as its control valve.

To make cylinder *A* go positive, an air signal is applied to the signal port 1 4 of control valve *A*. A push-button operated 3-port valve provides this 'start' signal when required (Fig. 8.5).

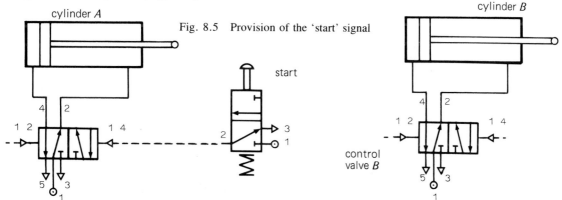

Fig. 8.5   Provision of the 'start' signal

When the start button is pressed and released, the first movement in the sequence is effected: cylinder *A* goes positive (Fig. 8.6). When cylinder *A* goes positive, the piston rod strikes the roller-trip 3-port valve *A*+. This produces an air signal which is used to initiate the next move in the sequence: *B*+. To do this, the signal from pilot valve *A*+ is routed to signal port 1 4 of control valve *B*. Control valve *B* makes cylinder *B* go positive.

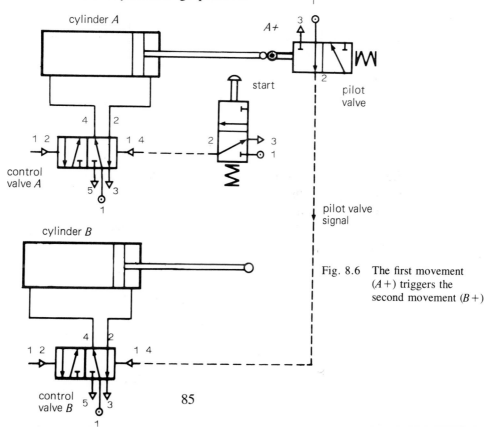

Fig. 8.6   The first movement
(*A*+) triggers the
second movement (*B*+)

85

When cylinder B goes positive, the piston rod strikes the roller-trip 3-port valve $B+$. This produces an air signal which is used to initiate the next move in the sequence: $A-$. The air signal is routed to signal port 1 2 of control valve A. The control valve A changes position and cylinder A goes negative (Fig. 8.7).

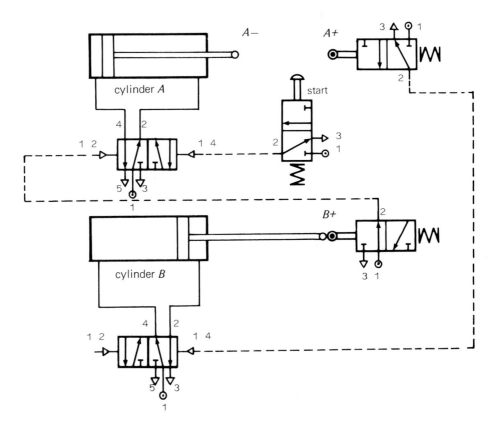

Fig. 8.7   The second movement $(B+)$ triggers the third movement $(A-)$

In Fig. 8.8, when cylinder A goes negative, the piston rod strikes the roller-trip 3-port valve $A-$. This produces an air signal which is used to initiate the last movement in the sequence: $B-$. The air signal is routed to signal port 1 2 of control valve B. Control valve B changes position and cylinder B goes negative. This completes the sequence of movements:

    start,
    cylinder $A+$,
    cylinder $B+$,
    cylinder $A-$,
    cylinder $B-$,
    stop.

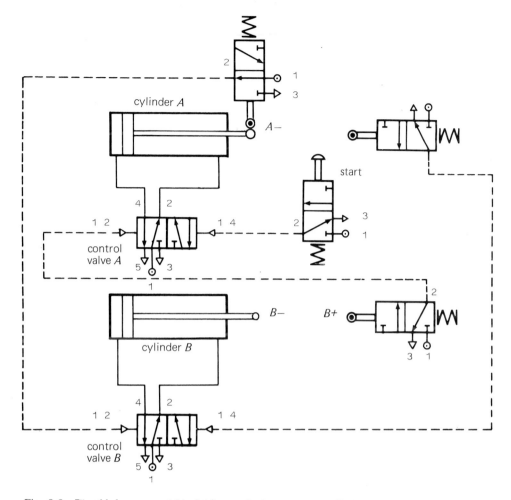

Fig. 8.8   The third movement ($A-$) triggers the last movement ($B-$)

■ Continuous Cycle Sequential Control

The circuit shown in Fig. 8.8 is started by pressing and releasing the push-button operated 3-port valve. The cylinders then perform the sequence of movements:

$A+$, $B+$, $A-$, $B-$, stop.

The sequence finishes with cylinder B in the negative position ($B-$). In some applications, it is desirable for the sequence to run continuously. This is achieved by using a roller-trip 3-port valve to detect the negative position ($B-$) of cylinder B. The signal from valve $B-$ is used to trigger the next cycle of sequential movements. In Fig. 8.9, the 'start' 3-port valve of Fig. 8.8 is replaced by a roller-trip operated 3-port valve $B-$.

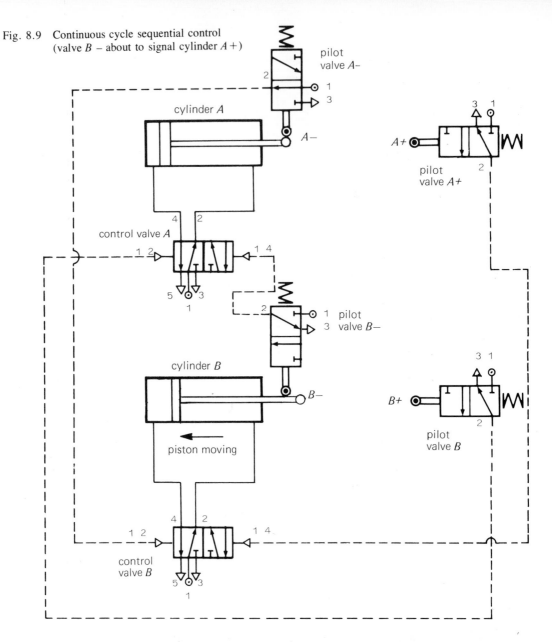

Fig. 8.9 Continuous cycle sequential control
(valve B – about to signal cylinder $A+$)

When main supply air is connected to the circuit, it operates continuously, repeating the cycle $A+$, $B+$, $A-$, $B-$

Although the cycle of cylinder movements is usually written in a straight line, a truer picture is shown by a circular diagram (Fig. 8.10). The cycle of cylinder movements can begin at any point in the circle and can be read clockwise as:

$$A+, B+, A-, B-$$
$$\text{or } B+, A-, B-, A+$$
$$\text{or } A-, B-, A+, B+$$
$$\text{or } B-, A+, B+, A-.$$

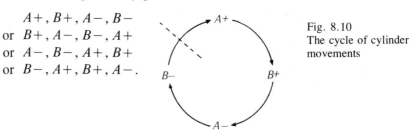

Fig. 8.10
The cycle of cylinder movements

The order of movements is the same in each case. The difference lies in the movement chosen to be first (or last) in the sequence. The cycle can be interrupted at any point by the insertion of a lever set/reset 3-port valve. For example, the cycle can begin with $A+$ and end with $B-$. To stop the sequence here, the signal from pilot valve $B-$ must be prevented from triggering cylinder A positive. A lever set/reset 3-port valve is connected in the pilot line between pilot valve $B-$ and signal port 1 4 of control valve A (Fig. 8.11).

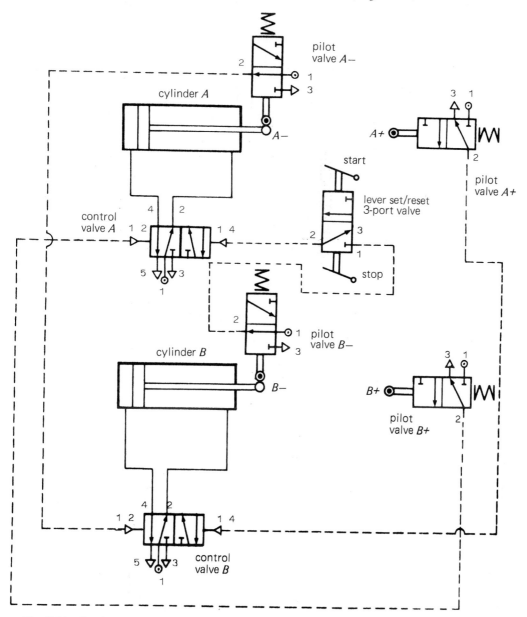

Fig. 8.11   Stop/start control of the continuous cycle sequential control circuit $A+$, $B+$, $A-$, $B-$ (the cylinder $A+$ signal from pilot valve $B-$ is inhibited by the stop/start valve)

■ Another Example of Sequential Control

Another sequence of cylinder movements is:

    start,

    cylinder $A+$,

    cylinder $B-$,

    cylinder $A-$,

    cylinder $B+$,

    stop.

This sequence can be written in a straight line:

    start, $A+$, $B-$, $A-$, $B+$, stop;

or drawn in the form of a circular diagram (Fig. 8.12) if the cycle is to be continuous.

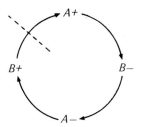

Fig. 8.12   Circular diagram of cylinder movements

A suitable circuit for this sequence is shown in Fig. 8.13.

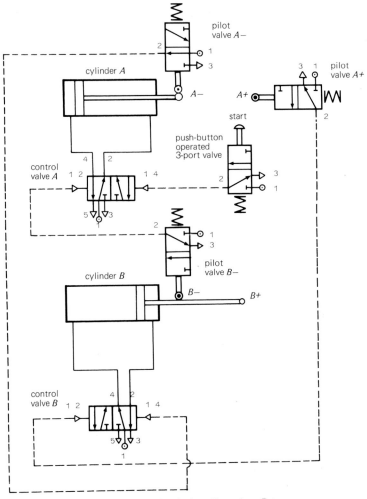

Fig. 8.13   Sequential control circuit $A+$, $B-$, $A-$, $B+$

90

When the push-button operated 3-port valve is pressed and released, a 'start' signal is routed to signal port 1 4 of control valve A. The control valve changes position, and cylinder A goes positive. The first stage $A+$ of the sequence is achieved.

The piston rod strikes the roller-trip of pilot valve $A+$. An air signal is routed to signal port 1 2 of control valve B. The control valve changes position, and cylinder B goes negative. The second stage $B-$ of the control sequence is achieved.

The piston rod of cylinder B strikes the roller-trip of pilot valve $B-$. An air signal is routed to signal port 1 2 of control valve A. The control valve changes position and cylinder A goes negative. The third stage $A-$ of the sequence is achieved.

Pilot valve $A-$ sends an air signal to the signal port 1 4 of control valve B. Control valve B changes position. Cylinder B goes positive. This completes the sequence.

If a repeating cycle is required, the 'start' push-button operated 3-port valve is replaced by a roller-trip valve. This is used as pilot valve $B+$ and a continuous cycle $A+$, $B-$, $A-$, $B+$ is produced (Fig. 8.14). If a lever set/reset 3-port valve is inserted in the pilot line between pilot valve $B+$ and control valve A, it is possible to stop the sequential cycle with cylinder $A-$ and cylinder $B+$ (Fig. 8.14).

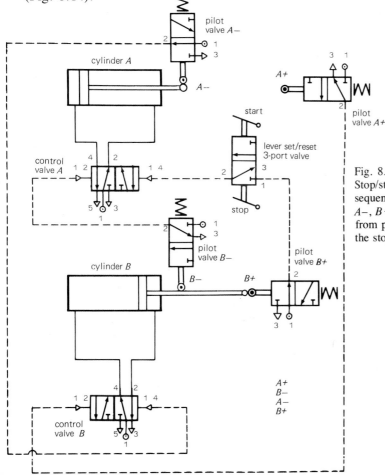

Fig. 8.14
Stop/start control of the continuous sequential control circuit $A+$, $B-$, $A-$, $B+$ (the cylinder $A+$ signal from pilot valve $B+$ is inhibited by the stop/start valve)

☐ Time Delay Sequential Control

In Chapter 7 a method of producing an automatic reciprocating circuit using two combinations of flow regulator and reservoir with a double-acting cylinder (Fig. 8.15) was described.

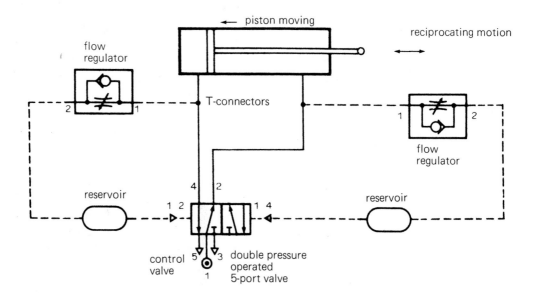

Fig. 8.15 Automatic control of a double-acting cylinder using reservoirs and flow regulators

The simple sequence of piston movements $A+$, $B+$, $A-$, $B-$ can be produced by modifying this circuit. Study the sequential control circuit shown in Fig. 8.16.

The sequence is started by pressing and releasing a push-button operated 3-port valve. This sends an air signal to signal port 1 4 of control valve A. Cylinder A goes positive when the control valve changes position. The first stage in the sequence is achieved. A T-connector at X also routes an air signal through a flow regulator and reservoir. These produce a time delay before the air signal changes the position of control valve B. Cylinder B now goes positive. This is the second stage of the sequence of piston rod movements $(B+)$. A T-connector at Y routes a time delayed air signal to control valve A. When the control valve changes position, cylinder A goes negative. The third stage of the sequence $(A-)$ is produced. A T-connector at Z routes a time delayed signal to control valve B. When control valve B changes position, cylinder B goes negative. This produces the final stage $(B-)$ in the sequence of piston movements.

The flow regulators require careful adjustment for satisfactory operation of the circuit. Reliable timing is necessary in sequential control and this can be difficult to establish in this circuit.

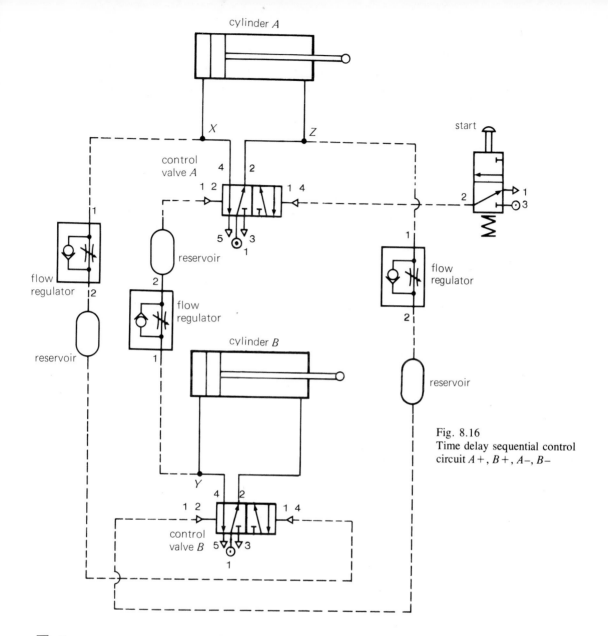

Fig. 8.16
Time delay sequential control
circuit $A+$, $B+$, $A-$, $B-$

☐ Sequential Control of Three Cylinders

Three cylinders A, B and C can be operated in a simple sequence. They must operate in the same sequence in the first and second halves of the cycle. A non-continuous sequence could be:

   start, $A+$, $B+$, $C+$, $A-$, $B-$, $C-$, stop.

If the sequence of piston movements is continuous, the cycle can be shown in circular form (Fig. 8.17).

Fig. 8.17   Continuous sequence of cylinders

The circuit for the sequence $A+$, $B+$, $C+$, $A-$, $B-$, $C-$ is shown in Fig. 8.18. A lever set/reset 3-port valve is used to give stop/start control. Study the circuit diagram carefully and consider how each stage is achieved.

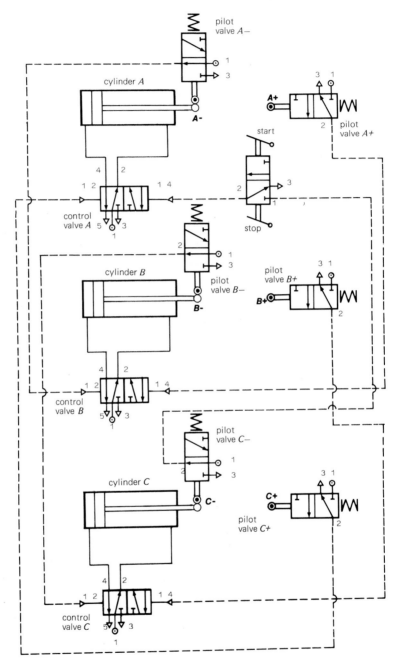

Fig. 8.18   Sequential control of three cylinders $A+$, $B+$, $C+$, $A-$, $B-$, $C-$ (the cylinder $A+$ signal from pilot valve $C-$ is inhibited by the stop/start valve)

9 Advanced Sequential Control

☐ An Application of Sequential Control

In the previous chapter two or more pneumatic cylinders operating in a pre-determined pattern or sequence were described. Sometimes the sequence was arranged to run continuously rather than complete one cycle and then stop. An application of sequential control of two cylinders is in pneumatically operating a drill and vice (Fig. 9.1).

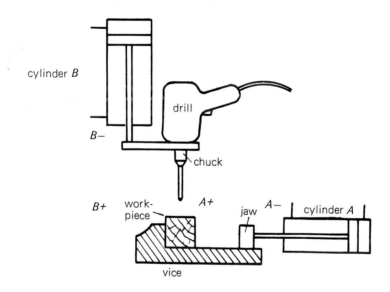

Fig. 9.1   Machine vice and power drill operation

Cylinder A operates a vice jaw to clamp the workpiece.
Cylinder B moves a power drill up and down. The sequence of movements is as follows.

1 The machine vice closes when cylinder A goes positive (Fig. 9.2, step 1).
2 The drill descends and bores a hole when cylinder B goes positive (Fig. 9.2, step 2).
3 The drill withdraws and returns to its original position when cylinder B goes negative (Fig. 9.2, step 3).
4 The vice opens to release the workpiece when cylinder A goes negative (Fig. 9.2, step 4).

Fig. 9.2 The steps of the sequential control of a machine vice and power drill

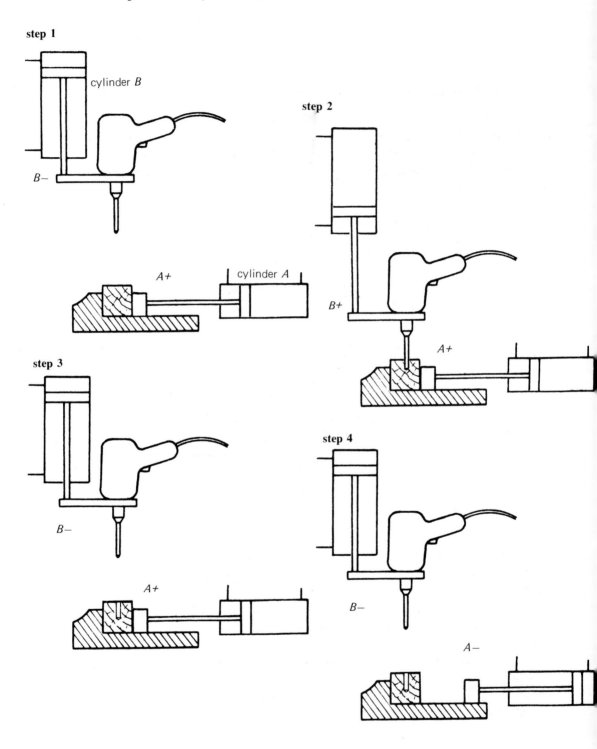

Stated simply, the sequence is:

$A+, B+, B-, A-.$

The cycle can be represented in circular form (Fig. 9.3).

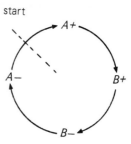

Fig. 9.3   The sequence in circular form

☐ An Inoperable Circuit

Chapter 8 dealt with simple pneumatic sequential control. In each half of a simple sequence, the cylinders operate in the same order. For example,

first half	second half
$A+, B+$	$A-, B-$
$A+, B-$	$A-, B+$
$A+, B+, C+$	$A-, B-, C-$

In the sequence for drill and vice control, the cylinders do not operate in the same order in each half of the cycle.

first half	second half
$A+, B+$	$B-, A-$

This sequence can be piped up as if it were a simple sequence. However, the circuit will not operate. This is because a double pressure operated 5-port valve ends up with a signal on both of its signal ports at the same time. It cannot respond to the second signal while the first one is still present. This is called an **inoperable circuit**. Figure 9.4 shows the problem.

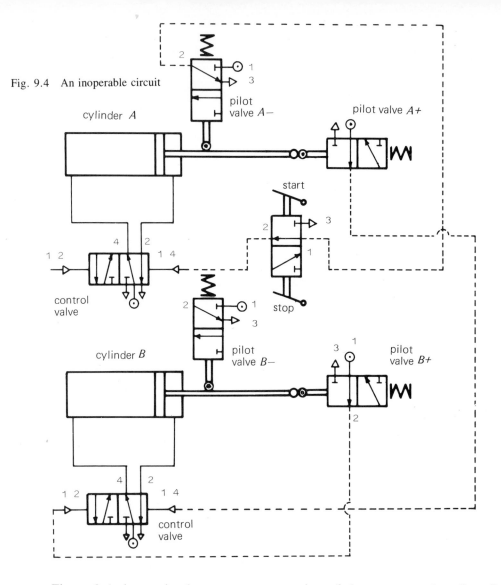

Fig. 9.4 An inoperable circuit

Figure 9.4 shows simple sequence connection of the sequence $A+$, $B+$, $B-$, $A-$ at the point where it has ceased to operate. The events leading to this were as follows.

1 Cylinder A moved positive, completing the first part of the sequence. Cylinder A tripped pilot valve $A+$. This signalled, and continues to signal, the second move in the sequence, cylinder B positive.

2 Pilot valve $A+$ signalled control valve B. Cylinder B moved positive, completing the second part of the sequence. Cylinder B tripped pilot valve $B+$. This signalled the third move in the sequence, cylinder B negative.

3 Pilot valve $B+$ signalled control valve B to make cylinder B move negative. But control valve B is still being signalled by pilot valve $A+$ to make cylinder B move positive. Result: everything has stopped as shown in Fig. 9.4. A way has to be found of removing the signal from pilot valve $A+$. Only then can control valve B respond to the signal from pilot valve $B+$.

☐ The Cascade System

A solution to the problem is to use the **cascade system**. This prevents old signals remaining in the circuit to oppose new signals. In the cascade system, the roller-trip pilot valves are supplied with main air only when they are required to produce a signal. The supply of air is then removed by a changeover valve. The pilot valves' main air supply arrangements are arrived at by dividing the sequence into **air groups**. The rule of air group division is that no alphabetic letter appears more than once in the group. In this case the groups are:

$$Group\ I \qquad Group\ II$$
$$A+, B+ \quad / \quad B-, A-.$$

Air groups are named with Roman numerals and separated by an oblique stroke. The letters in the two air groups refer, of course, to piston movements. In designing a cascade system, the letters also refer to the roller-trip 3-port valves. The two valves in Group I ($A+$ and $B+$) have one source of main air supply. The two valves in Group II ($B-$ and $A-$) have another source of main air supply. The Group II supply is turned 'off' when the Group I supply is turned 'on' and vice versa.

The pilot valves in each group are all connected to a group main air supply feeder unit called a **busbar**. The busbars are drawn in a circuit diagram as shown in Fig. 9.5.

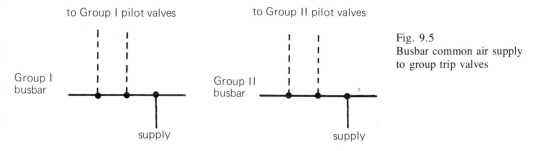

to Group I pilot valves   to Group II pilot valves

Group I busbar

Group II busbar

supply

supply

Fig. 9.5
Busbar common air supply
to group trip valves

In a sequential control circuit with two cylinders, four-way connectors can be used as busbars. Sequential control circuits with several cylinders often use manifolds as busbars. A **manifold** is a long connector with several air tappings (Fig. 9.6).

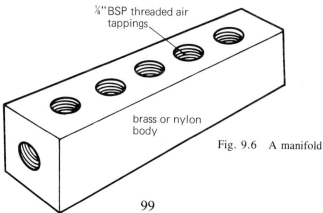

⅛" BSP threaded air tappings

brass or nylon body

Fig. 9.6   A manifold

99

Main air is supplied to each busbar from an outlet of a double pressure operated 5-port valve. It is known as the **group changeover valve**. It supplies one busbar at a time and is connected to them as shown in Fig. 9.7.

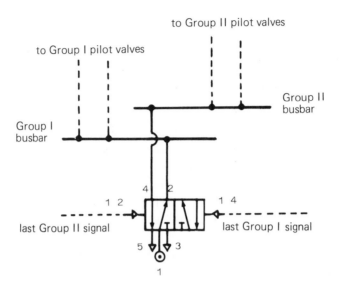

Fig. 9.7 Group changeover valve

Air **group selection** is achieved by signalling the group changeover valve. A signal from the last pilot valve in Group II $(A-)$ to signal port 1 2 selects Group I air supply. A signal from the last pilot valve in Group I $(B+)$ selects Group II air supply. The last pilot valve in each air group is often called the **group selector valve.**

   As with all pneumatic circuits, a careful, step by step approach is required for successful connection of a cascaded sequential control circuit. For the sequence $A+, B+/B-, A-$, this would be as follows.

   Step 1 Connect the main air to all three 5-port valves.

   Step 2 Connect the group air supplies. Valves $A+$ and $B+$ to Group I. Valves $B-$ and $A-$ to Group II (Fig. 9.8).

   Step 3 Connect the last signal from Group I $(B+)$ and the last signal from Group II $(A-)$ to the group changeover valve (Fig. 9.8).

Notice that the first piston movement in each group $(A+$ and $B-)$ is signalled directly from the group busbar. For example, the signal for $A+$ is applied to signal port 1 4 of control valve A directly from Group I busbar. The signal for $B-$ is applied to signal port 1 2 of control valve B directly from Group II busbar (Fig. 9.9).

100

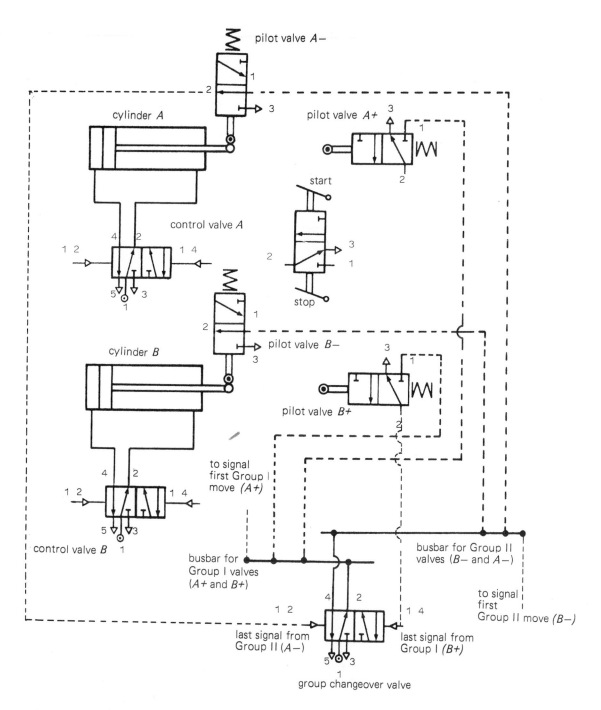

Fig. 9.8 Connection of the air supplies to each group of trip valves

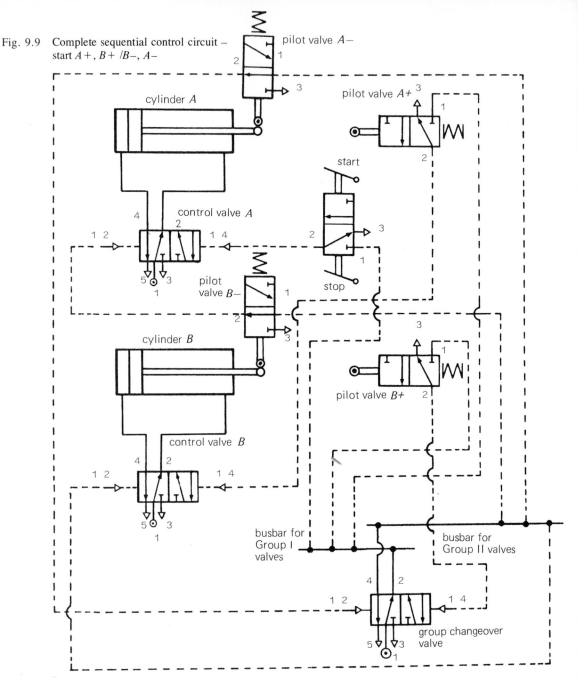

Fig. 9.9 Complete sequential control circuit – start $A+$, $B+$ /$B-$, $A-$

pilot valve $A-$

cylinder A

pilot valve $A+$

control valve A

start

pilot valve $B-$

stop

cylinder B

pilot valve $B+$

control valve B

busbar for Group I valves

busbar for Group II valves

group changeover valve

When the lever set/reset 3-port valve is moved to 'start', an air signal is sent to signal port 1 4 of control valve A. Cylinder A goes positive and the piston rod trips valve $A+$. The first step of the sequence ($A+$) has been achieved.

The next step in the sequence of piston movements is $B+$. The air signal from valve $A+$ is connected to signal port 1 4 of control valve B. Cylinder B goes positive and the piston rod trips valve $B+$. The second step of the sequence ($B+$) has been achieved.

102

Pilot valves $A+$ and $B+$ are supplied with Group I air. The Group I stages of the sequence are complete. Group I air has to be cut off and Group II air has to be selected. The signal from pilot valve $B+$ is connected to the group change-over valve. The changeover valve moves position. Main air is supplied to the Group II valves, $B-$ and $A-$.

The next step in the sequence of piston movements is $B-$. An air signal from the Group II busbar is taken to the signal port 1 2 of control valve B. Cylinder B goes negative and the piston rod trips valve $B-$. The third step of the sequence $(B-)$ has been achieved.

The next step in the sequence of piston movements is $A-$. An air signal from valve $B-$ is connected to signal port 1 2 of control valve A. Cylinder A now goes negative and the piston rod trips valve $A-$. The last step in the sequence $(A-)$ has been achieved.

The Group II stages of the sequence are complete. To repeat the cycle, the air signal from valve $A-$ is connected to the group changeover valve. This cuts off Group II air and turns on Group I air. When the changeover valve moves position, an air signal from Group I busbar passes through the 'stop/start' valve to signal port 1 4 of control valve A. The cycle repeats and continues until the lever set/reset 3-port valve is moved to 'stop'.

☐ Another Example of the Cascade System

An apparently more difficult sequence of piston movements is: start, $A+$, $A-$, $B+$, $B-$.

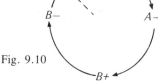

Step 1 Divide the sequence into air groups.
Each letter can only appear once in each air group.

    Group I   Group II Group III
    start, $A+$ / $A-$, $B+$ / $B-$

Fig. 9.10

Division into three air groups is not necessary because the sequence is a cycle. Figure 9.10 shows how the end of the cycle joins on to the beginning. It can be seen that exactly the same sequence of piston movements can be written out as:

$B-$, start, $A+$, $A-$, $B+$.

Air group division is now:

    Group I   Group II
    $B-$, start, $A+$ / $A-$, $B+$

Step 2 Draw the circuit.
Draw the busbar lines for
each air group. Connect
the busbar to a group
changeover valve.

Fig. 9.11   The group changeover valve

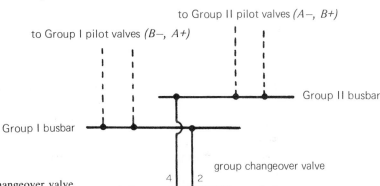

103

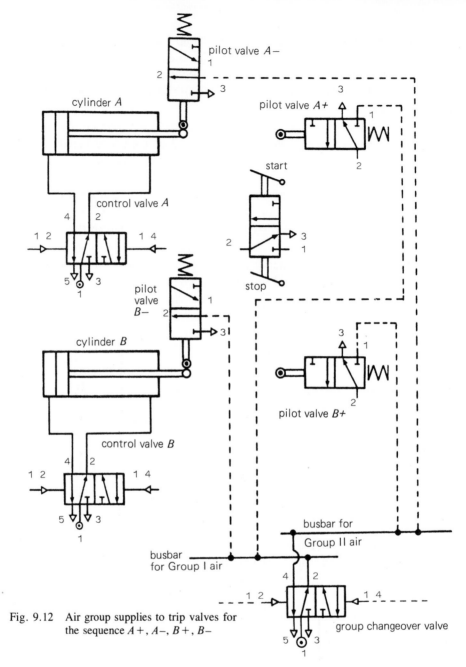

Fig. 9.12 Air group supplies to trip valves for
the sequence $A+$, $A-$, $B+$, $B-$

Step 3 Connect the busbars to each group of pilot valves (Fig. 9.12). This provides the common air supply to each group of roller-trip valves. Group I air is supplied to trip valves $B-$ and $A+$. Group II air is supplied to trip valves $A-$ and $B+$.

Step 4 Beginning with 'start', work round the circuit in the required sequence. The start signal is connected to control valve A (Fig. 9.13). Cylinder A goes positive. The signal from trip valve $A+$ is connected to port 1 4 of the group changeover valve. Group I air is cut off. Group II air is turned on.

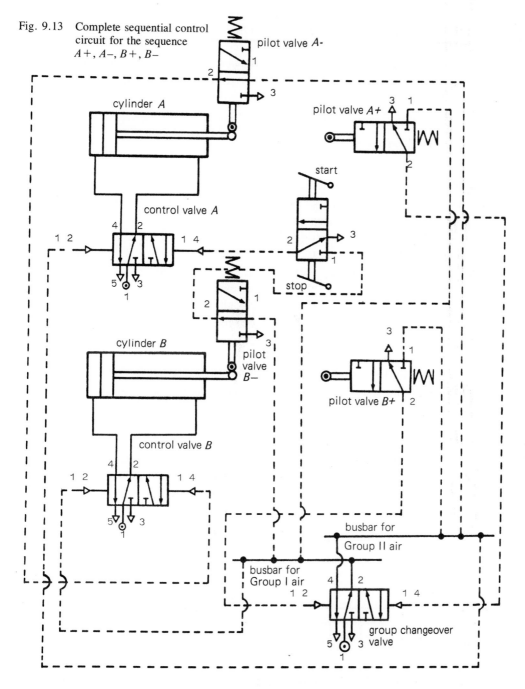

Fig. 9.13 Complete sequential control circuit for the sequence $A+, A-, B+, B-$

pilot valve A-

cylinder A

pilot valve A+

control valve A

start

stop

pilot valve B-

cylinder B

pilot valve B+

control valve B

busbar for Group II air

busbar for Group I air

group changeover valve

Step 5 A signal from Group II busbar is connected to signal port 1 2 of control valve A. Cylinder A goes negative.

Step 6 A signal from trip valve $A-$ is connected to signal port 1 4 of control valve B. Cylinder B goes positive.

Step 7 A signal from trip valve $B+$ is connected to signal port 1 2 of the group changeover valve. Group II air is cut off. Group I air is turned on.

Step 8 A signal from Group I busbar is connected to signal port 1 2 of control valve *B*. Cylinder *B* goes negative.

Step 9 A signal from trip valve *B−* is connected through the 'stop/start' valve to signal port 1 4 of control valve *A*. This completes the sequence *A+*, *A−*, *B+*, *B−*.

☐ Sequential Control of Three Cylinders

Consider the sequential control of three cylinders, cylinder *A*, cylinder *B* and cylinder *C*. Some three-cylinder sequential control circuits have a sequence of movements that divides into two air groups. For example, the sequence *A+*, *B+*, *C+*, *A−*, *C−*, *B−* divides as:

Group I	Group II
A+, *B+*, *C+* /	*A−*, *C−*, *B−*

Notice that each letter appears only once in each air group. A cylinder can only make one movement in each air group.

Some three-cylinder sequential control circuits have a sequence of cylinder movements that divides into three air groups, for example, the sequence:

start, *A+*, *B+*, *B−*, *C+*, *C−*, *A−*.

This sequence can be described in circular form (Fig. 9.14).

Step 1 Divide the sequence of cylinder movements into air groups.

Group I	Group II	Group III
A+, *B+* /	*B−*, *C+* /	*C−*, *A−*

Step 2 Draw the circuit. Draw the busbars for each air group. Connect the busbars to group changeover valves. When the sequence is divided into three air groups, there are two group changeover valves. Figure 9.15 shows how the group changeover valves are arranged in a cascade system.

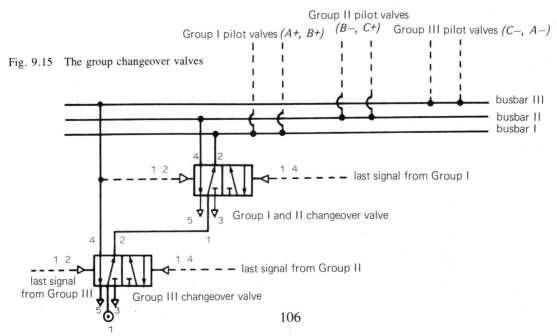

Fig. 9.14

Fig. 9.15 The group changeover valves

Signalling the group changeover valves allows each busbar to be individually selected to supply air to Group I or Group II or Group III.

Step 3   Group I busbar is connected to supply air to pilot valves $A+$ and $B+$. Group II busbar is connected to supply air to pilot valves $B-$ and $C+$. Group III busbar is connected to supply air to pilot valves $C-$ and $A-$ (Fig. 9.16).

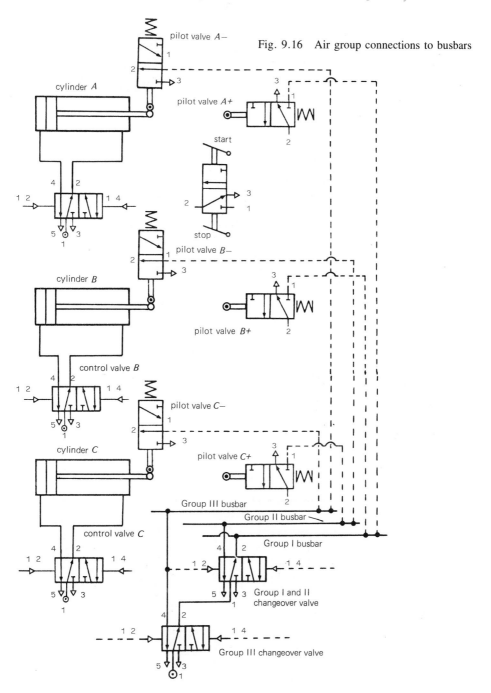

Fig. 9.16   Air group connections to busbars

Step 4 The start signal is connected to signal port 1 4 of control valve *A* (Fig. 9.17). Cylinder *A* goes positive. The signal from valve *A*+ is connected to signal port 1 4 of control valve *B*. Cylinder *B* goes positive.

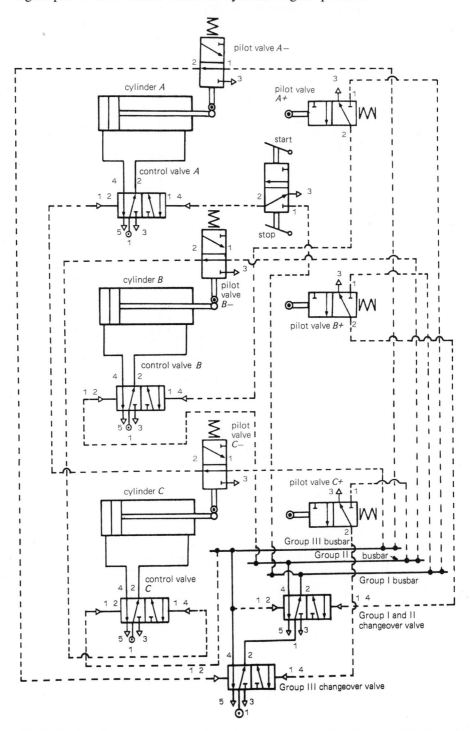

Fig. 9.17   Complete sequential control circuit for the sequence $A+$, $B+$, $B-$, $C+$, $C-$, $A-$

Step 5   The air signal from valve $B+$ is connected to signal port 1 4 of Group I and II changeover valve. This selects Group II air to supply valves $B-$ and $C+$.

Step 6   An air signal is taken from the Group II busbar to signal port 1 2 of control valve B. Cylinder B goes negative.

Step 7   An air signal from valve $B-$ is connected to signal port 1 4 of control valve C. Cylinder C goes positive. An air signal from valve $C+$ is connected to signal port 1 4 of the Group III changeover valve. The valve selects the Group III busbar.

Step 8   An air signal is taken from Group III busbar to signal port 1 2 of control valve C. Cylinder C goes negative. An air signal from valve $C-$ is connected to signal port 1 2 of control valve A. Cylinder A goes negative.

Step 9   An air signal from valve $A-$ is connected to signal port 1 2 of the Group III changeover valve. The cascade system of changeover valves selects the Group I busbar.

A T-connector after port 4 of Group III changeover valve allows air to reach signal port 1 2 of Group I and II changeover valve. The supply of air to the Group III busbar automatically resets the other changeover valve ready to supply air to Group I busbar when the changeover signal arrives, i.e. when an air signal from valve $A-$ reaches port 1 2 of the Group III changeover valve.

Step 10   An air signal is taken from the Group I busbar through the lever set/reset, stop/start valve to signal port 1 4 of control valve A. This completes the sequence $A+$, $B+$, / $B-$, $C+$ / $C-$, $A-$.

10 Air Jet Devices and Systems

■ Sensing Systems

To detect when a piston rod has completed its stroke, a pneumatic valve with a mechanical operating mechanism, e.g. plunger or roller-trip, is frequently used. The piston rod has to make contact with the sensing device, the valve. In some situations, this detection system has two serious disadvantages.

1 It may be undesirable or impossible to position a roller-trip or plunger operated valve close to a piston rod, component or machine part.

2 Considerable force is required to operate roller-trip or plunger mechanisms.

The disadvantages can be overcome in two ways.

1 By devising a sensing system which
   (a) still requires contact with say, a piston rod, but
   (b) is smaller and requires less operating force.

2 By devising a **contactless sensing system**.

In Chapter 5, air bleed control of pneumatic circuits was described. The air bleed principle has been considerably developed from this simple beginning and a large range of control systems are based on it. These systems overcome many of the problems of signalling with mechanical valves. They also open up quite new control possibilities. However, many of these systems require a special low pressure supply of oil-free air.

■ Low Pressure Supply of Oil-free Air

The airways in many low pressure devices are very small and are easily clogged by dirt and oil. An **oil-free supply** of clean, dry air is essential. The oil-free air is obtained by tapping into the high pressure air line after its filter and regulator but before the lubricator. Additional filtering with a super-fine, oil removing filter (Fig. 10.1a) is essential before the oil-free air is fed to a pressure regulator and the rest of the low pressure system.

An oil-free supply of air is shown by the symbol ──●

A lubricated supply is indicated by ──⊙ .

The low pressure supply is controlled by a suitable **pressure regulator**. The regulator is fitted with a gauge reading from 0–2 bar (Fig. 10.1b)

Fig. 10.1   (a) A 'Puraire' filter   (b) A pressure regulator fitted with a gauge

The circuit diagram symbol for a pressure regulator with gauge is shown in Fig. 10.2.

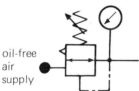

oil-free air supply

Fig. 10.2   Circuit diagram symbol for pressure regulator with gauge

Many low pressure systems require further air flow control. The unidirectional flow regulator from the main Pneumatics kit is used for this purpose.

Low air pressures can be measured in **bars** or **millibars (mbar)**. 1000 millibars = 1 bar, i.e. 1000 mbar = 1 bar. A pressure of 1 bar is about the pressure of the atmosphere and equals 10^5 newtons per square metre or 10^5 pascals.

1 Where have you heard atmospheric pressure referred to in millibars?

2 How many millibars are there in 0.7 bar?

3 How many bars is 10 millibars?

■ Air Bleed Jet Occlusion Systems

An air bleed jet occlusion system can be used to sense the presence of a component, the position of a machine or the end of a cylinder's stroke. The sensor consists of a small hole through which a jet of air is allowed to bleed to atmosphere (Fig. 10.3).

Fig. 10.3   Jet occlusion system

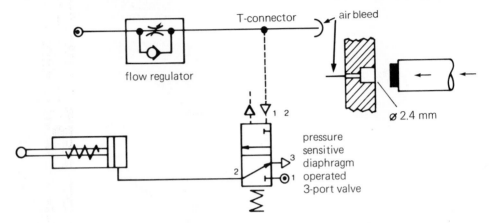

This system was shown in Chapter 5. When the jet bleeds to atmosphere, the pressure above the 3-port valve's diaphragm is low. If the jet is covered over, or **occluded**, there is an immediate pressure build-up in the signal line to the valve. The pressure, acting on the diaphragm, causes the 3-port valve to turn 'on' and admit high pressure air to the single-acting cylinder. The single-acting cylinder outstrokes.

The air jet bleeds through a 2.4 mm diameter hole. Alternatively, the air can bleed through an **emitter** (Fig. 10.16a). To ensure the jet is occluded and does not leak, a seal made of rubber can be fitted to the moving part (Fig. 10.4a). Alternative methods of occluding the jet are shown in Fig. 10.4b and c.

Fig. 10.4   Various mechanical methods of occluding air jets

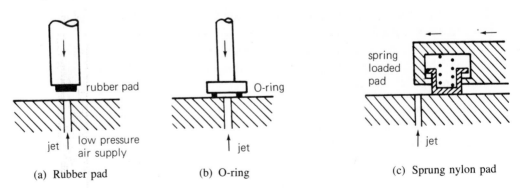

(a) Rubber pad   (b) O-ring   (c) Sprung nylon pad

An air jet can be occluded by a finger pressed over the jet orifice. A special **touch sensor** is made for this purpose (Fig. 10.5).

Fig. 10.5 (a) Touch sensor

(b) Circuit diagram symbol for a touch sensor

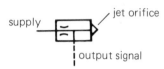

For reasons of economy, it is desirable to keep the signal air supply pressure very low so that the flow of air bleeding to atmosphere is very small. However, this makes the response of the standard 3-port diaphragm valve sluggish and even unreliable when the jet is occluded. A fast, snappy response can be regained by replacing the standard 3-port diaphragm valve with a sensitive diaphragm controlled amplifier valve (Fig. 10.6). An **amplifier valve**, or **step-up relay**, responds to a very low pressure signal (5 mbar) and so controls the flow of high pressure air in a pneumatic circuit. The pressure signal to a 'Boostermite' must not exceed 0.3 bar.

Fig. 10.6 (a) An amplifier valve or step-up relay –
the low pressure 'Boostermite'

(b) Circuit diagram symbol

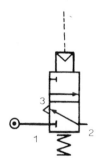

Figure 10.7 shows a touch sensor being used with an amplifier valve in a jet occlusion circuit. In such a circuit, the signal tube between the sensor and the signal port of the amplifier valve should be kept as short as possible so that there is minimum time delay before a response to a signal is obtained.

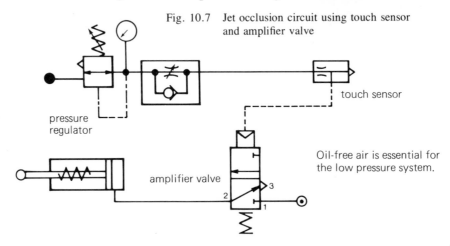

Fig. 10.7   Jet occlusion circuit using touch sensor and amplifier valve

More than one sensor can be used in a system. Figure 10.8 shows a series of touch sensors controlling a combination door lock. All five sensors must be occluded together in order to draw the door bolt. This is a logic 'AND' system. Notice that the circuit uses a sprung outstroke single-acting cylinder. Study the circuit carefully and note how it works.

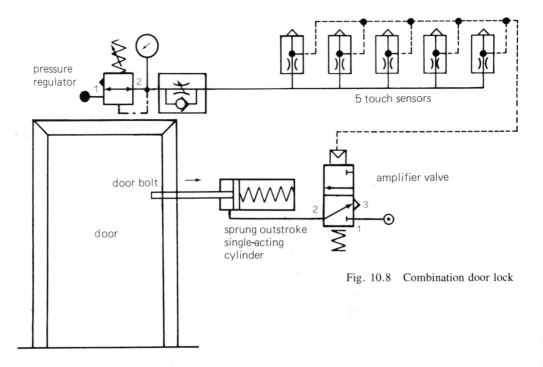

Fig. 10.8   Combination door lock

114

■ Contactless Sensing Systems

In earlier chapters several examples have been given of the control of a pneumatic cylinder without any contact between the piston rod and a pilot valve. One such example used a diaphragm operated 3-port valve (Fig. 10.9). The diaphragm valve senses exhaust pressure decay and signals the cylinder to instroke automatically after it has outstroked.

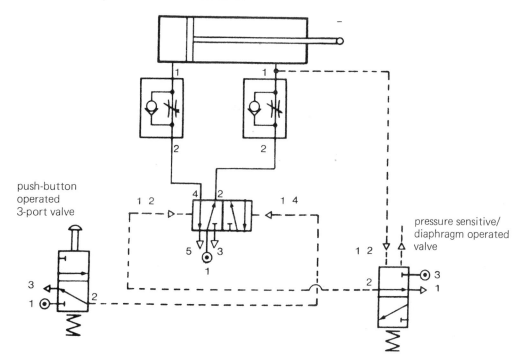

This circuit has been fully described in Chapter 5. A pressure rise sensing system was described in Chapter 6. Revise this earlier work. These systems are useful but they have limitations which make them unsuitable for many applications. Much more useful, non-automatic, contactless sensing systems can be made up using air jets and various types of sensor.

■ The Proximity Sensor

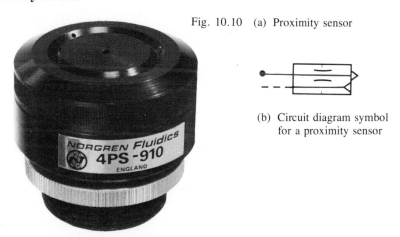

Fig. 10.10   (a) Proximity sensor

(b) Circuit diagram symbol
for a proximity sensor

This is a contactless sensing device which detects the presence of an object brought close to it. It operates from a low pressure, oil-free air supply.

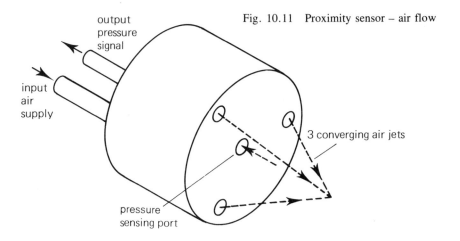

Fig. 10.11   Proximity sensor – air flow

The air supplied to the proximity sensor issues from three orifices as three converging jets (Fig. 10.11). The air jets impinge on a passing object, but the jets are not occluded as the object does not touch the sensor. Instead, a small, localised air pressure rise results between the object and the sensor (Fig. 10.12). This causes a pressure rise in the sensor's pressure sensing port, and a pressure signal appears at the device's output port. The pressure signal output is routed to an amplifier valve which turns on the high pressure supply of a pneumatic circuit (Fig. 10.12).

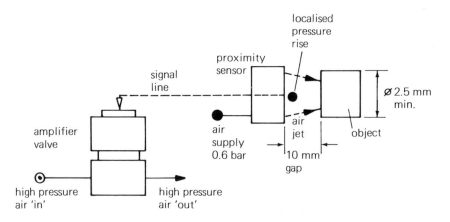

Fig. 10.12   Typical circuit for a proximity sensor

With a supply pressure of 0.6 bar, the proximity sensor reliably detects objects 10 mm away from it, provided the objects are not smaller than 25 mm diameter. Figure 10.13 shows a proximity sensor being used in a system which counts packages moving on a conveyor belt.

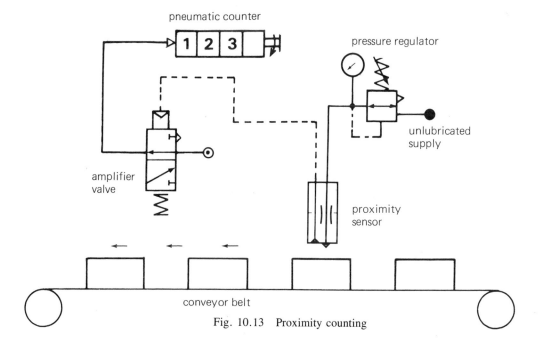

Fig. 10.13   Proximity counting

■ Fluid Flow

Gases and liquids are both fluids. The special properties of a flowing fluid (in this case, air) can be used for sensing, amplification and logic tasks. An example of the latter will be given in Chapter 11. In industry, these tasks are often performed by electronic devices. However, these devices have limitations. They cannot withstand extremes of heat or cold, high acceleration, shock, vibration or nuclear radiation. Fluid based devices are not affected by harsh environments. They have been used in missiles, rockets and space modules as well as in more ordinary industrial applications. Their safety makes them specially suitable for use in dangerous situations, e.g. petroleum and explosives manufacturing plants.

    4 Why are fluid based control systems to be preferred to electrical or electronic based ones in an explosives factory?

When a fluid flows through a smooth pipe, the fluid particles move in stream lines or layers which flow over one another. The particles do not move between layers. This is called layer or **laminar flow**.

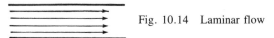

Fig. 10.14   Laminar flow

A fluid issuing from a pipe in a jet will move with laminar flow for a distance of up to one hundred times the diameter of the pipe bore, provided the velocity of the stream of fluid is kept low (Fig. 10.15a).

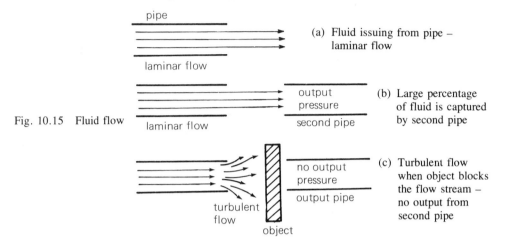

Fig. 10.15   Fluid flow

(a) Fluid issuing from pipe – laminar flow

(b) Large percentage of fluid is captured by second pipe

(c) Turbulent flow when object blocks the flow stream – no output from second pipe

If a second pipe is held in the jet stream a short distance in front of the first pipe, a large percentage of the fluid is captured by the second pipe (Fig. 10.15b). There is a pressure rise in the second pipe which can be used as an output signal to drive an amplifier valve or some other device.

If an object interrupts the fluid stream, the flow becomes turbulent. The fluid particles move about with random velocities. There is no pressure rise in the second pipe and therefore no output signal (Fig. 10.15c). This behaviour of a fluid is used in an **interruptible jet system**.

■ Interruptible Jet Systems

An interruptible jet system consists of an **emitter** (Fig. 10.16a) and a **collector** (Fig. 10.16b).

Fig. 10.16   (a) Emitter and circuit symbol

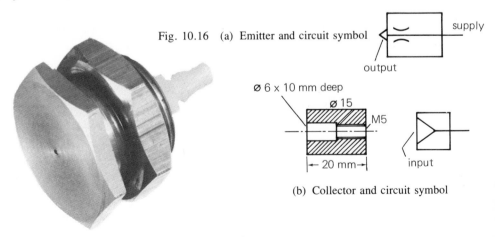

(b) Collector and circuit symbol

The emitter is supplied with low pressure air. An air jet from the emitter flows across a gap and is received by the collector (Fig. 10.17). Pressure rises in the collector and it produces a pressure signal at its output port. The pressure signal is routed to an amplifier valve which is held in the 'on' state by the signal. If an object interrupts the air flow across the gap, the pressure signal is removed and the amplifier valve switches 'off'.

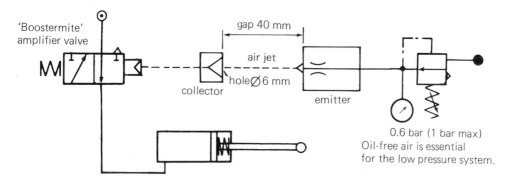

Fig. 10.17   Interruptible jet system

The size of the gap across which the interruptible jet sensor system will operate reliably is determined by the supply pressure to the emitter and the sensitivity of the amplifier valve. With the kit equipment and a supply pressure of 0.6 bar, a gap of 40 mm is possible.

Fig. 10.18   (a) Interruptible jet sensor

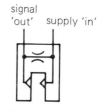

(b) Circuit diagram symbol

119

An **interruptible jet sensor** is a device which has a collector and emitter machined in a U-shaped block (Fig. 10.18). Figure 10.19 shows how it is connected into a low pressure circuit to be used as a sensing device for the control of a high pressure pneumatic system.

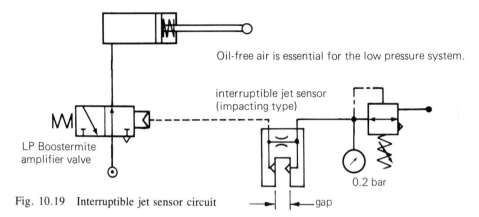

Fig. 10.19   Interruptible jet sensor circuit

This sensor can be used for many purposes, e.g. detecting small, fragile components, scale pointers, the edge of materials or soft fabrics, the end of a roll of sheet material.

■ Dusty Atmospheres

Some environments are problematic for jet detection systems. The collector can become clogged if it is in the dusty atmosphere of a sawmill, cement works or a flour mill. To prevent clogging, the collector is pressurised (Fig. 10.20). A continuous flow of air out of the collector is arranged to blow away any dust which would otherwise settle on the collector and block it. The pressure of the air supplied to the collector must, of course, be below the operating pressure of the amplifier valve.

Fig. 10.20   Interruptible jet with pressurised collector

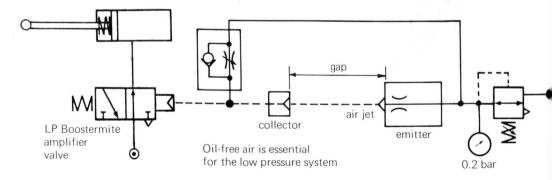

The interruptible jet sensor in the low pressure equipment kit has a pressurised collector. Its circuit diagram symbol (Fig. 10.18b) indicates how this is arranged in the device. A device with this facility is sometimes called an **impacting jet sensor**.

■ Long Distance Gap Sensor

The interruptible jet systems described so far have been used to detect when an object has interrupted the laminar flow of air from one pipe across a gap and into another pipe (Fig. 10.21a). The object causes turbulence and there is no output pressure in the output tube.

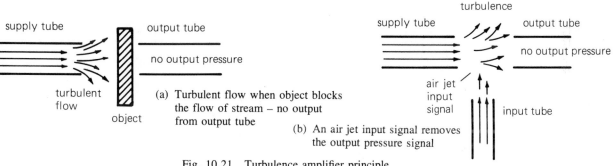

Fig. 10.21   Turbulence amplifier principle

If the object is replaced with another jet of air, turbulence is also caused. Again, there is no output pressure in the output tube (Fig. 10.21b). This phenomenon is used in the **turbulence amplifier**. A turbulence amplifier is a device with a supply tube, one or more input tubes and an output tube. It is a small device and was used extensively in **fluid logic (fluidic)** control systems.

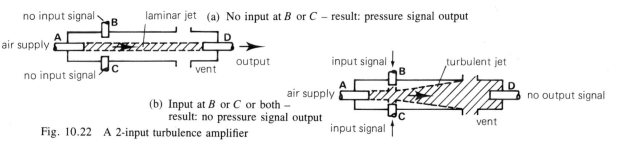

Fig. 10.22   A 2-input turbulence amplifier

When there is no air input signal at B or C (Fig. 10.22a) there is a pressure signal output from output tube D. If an air signal is applied at B or C or both, the air jet issuing from tube A becomes turbulent and there is no pressure signal output from tube D (Fig. 10.22b). This 2-input turbulence amplifier performs the 'NOR' (i.e. NOT OR) logic function because, when there is an input at B OR C OR both, there is NOT a pressure signal output from tube D.

The turbulence amplifier principle can be used as a sensing system for working across long distance gaps.

air supply

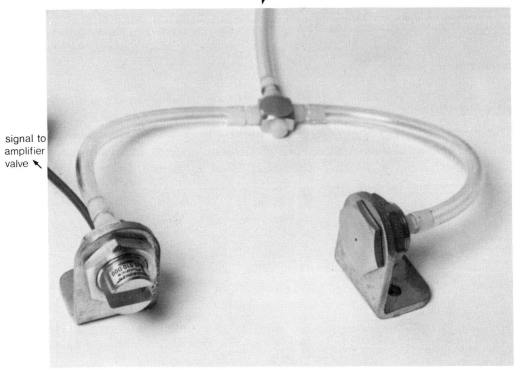

signal to
amplifier
valve

Fig. 10.23 (a) A long distance gap sensing system

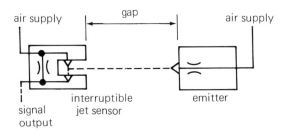

air supply   gap   air supply

signal
output   interruptible   emitter
           jet sensor

(b) Circuit diagram symbols for long distance gap sensing system

A long distance gap sensing system can be made up with the interruptible jet
sensor and the emitter (Fig. 10.23). The two devices are separated by the gap
over which sensing is to take place. The interruptible jet sensor is the equivalent
of the turbulence amplifier's supply and output tubes. The emitter is the equivalent of the turbulence amplifier's input tube. The jet from the emitter is aimed at
the interruptible jet sensor's jet and causes it to become turbulent. As a result
there is no pressure signal output from the interruptible jet sensor. If the emitter's jet is interrupted by an object, the interruptible jet sensor's jet becomes
laminar again and there is now an output pressure signal from the interruptible
jet sensor.

122

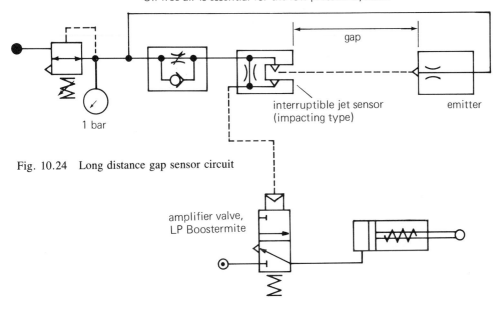

Oil-free air is essential for the low pressure system.

gap

interruptible jet sensor
(impacting type)

emitter

1 bar

Fig. 10.24   Long distance gap sensor circuit

amplifier valve,
LP Boostermite

The long distance gap sensing system (Fig. 10.24) can cover gaps in excess of 300 mm. The reliability of the system can be upset if strong draughts disturb the air jet from the emitter. The system has many uses. For example, the emitter can be placed on one side of a conveyor belt with the interruptible jet sensor on the other side. Large packages passing along the conveyor belt interrupt the emitter's air stream. This causes the interruptible jet sensor to give an output pressure signal. This signal could operate an amplifier valve which could oper- ate a pneumatic counter.

■ Connecting Low Pressure Devices

The ports of the low pressure devices in the kit are equipped with barbed fittings (Fig. 10.25). ⅛'' or ¹⁄₁₆'' internal diameter PVC tube is pushed over the barbed fittings to connect devices together. Generally, the ⅛'' bore tube is used for air supply and the ¹⁄₁₆'' bore tube for signals.

Fig. 10.25   Barbed connectors for ⅛''
and ¹⁄₁₆'' bore PVC tube

Two or more tubes of the same or different bore can be joined by making up a connector from the appropriate barbed fittings and an aluminium cross-piece. Plugs are screwed into any unused ports in the cross-piece (Fig. 10.26).

Fig. 10.26

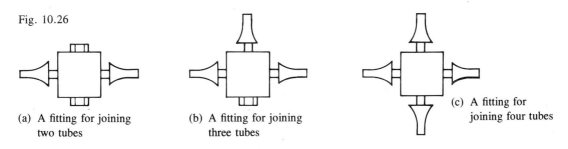

(a) A fitting for joining
two tubes

(b) A fitting for joining
three tubes

(c) A fitting for
joining four tubes

Figure 10.27 shows a method of connecting nylon high pressure tube to the jet orifice in a jet occlusion system.

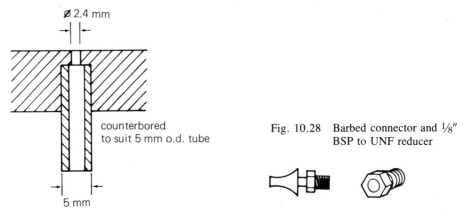

Fig. 10.27   Push-in-tube connection

Fig. 10.28   Barbed connector and ⅛″ BSP to UNF reducer

Equipment with ⅛″ BSP ports can be connected to the ⅛″ or ¹⁄₁₆″ bore tube with a ⅛″ BSP to UNF reducer and the appropriate barbed connector (Fig. 10.28). However, the ⅛″ and ¹⁄₁₆″ bore PVC tube must on no account be used with high pressure air.

The ⅛″ and ¹⁄₁₆″ barbed connectors have a unified fine (UNF) thread. The thread dimensions are very similar to an M5 thread and the one will screw into the other if need arises and UNF taps are not available.

Answers to Questions
1 In weather forecasts.
2 700 mbar.
3 0.01 bar.
4 Because the risk of a spark or overheating which could cause a fire or explosion is eliminated.

11 Air Jet Applications and Logic Circuits

■ Air Jet System Applications

An interruptible jet sensor can be used to detect coins put into a slot. The interruptible jet sensor's position can be adjusted so that it is only activated by coins of the correct size. Figure 11.1 shows a circuit which uses this system to signal the outstroke of a double-acting cylinder.

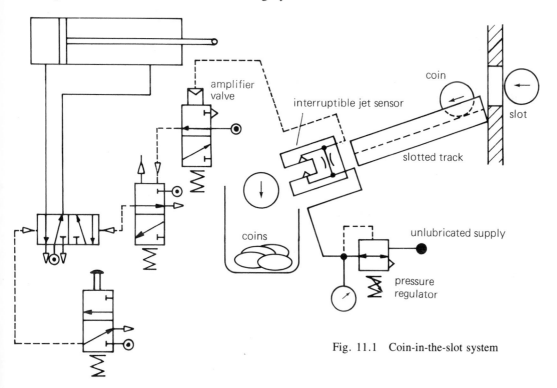

Fig. 11.1   Coin-in-the-slot system

Air streaming across the interruptible jet sensor holds an amplifier valve in the 'on' position. Its output holds a 'normally on' diaphragm valve 'off'. A coin placed in the slot rolls down a track. If the coin is the correct diameter, it interrupts the sensor's air jet. When this happens, the amplifier valve moves to the 'off' position and the signal is removed from the diaphragm valve. This moves to the 'on' position. The output from the diaphragm valve signals the double pressure operated 5-port valve. The double-acting cylinder outstrokes.

A system for counting large objects, such as people entering a room, is shown in Fig. 11.2. A hairdryer or a hose attached to the 'blow end' of a cylinder vacuum cleaner can be used to provide an air stream to interrupt a sensor's air jet. The sensor is connected to an amplifier valve which controls high pressure air to a pneumatic counter. When the air stream is interrupted by a large object, the counter is advanced one digit.

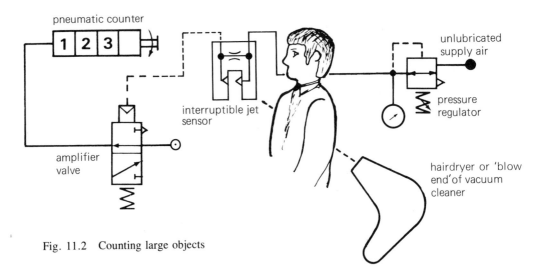

Fig. 11.2   Counting large objects

A similar gap sensor circuit can be used to count the number of revolutions of an electric motor (Fig. 11.3). A rotor or two-blade fan fixed to the motor spindle is rotated by the motor. The rotor will interrupt the sensor's jet twice in every revolution.

Fig. 11.3   Counting circuit – interruptible jet

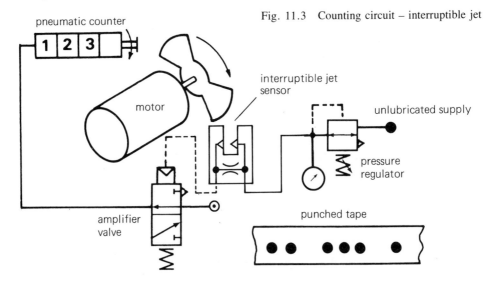

The low pressure air pulses from the sensor pass to the amplifier valve. This device outputs pulses of high pressure air which advance the counter.

1 How would you measure the speed of the electric motor in revs/min?

The low pressure circuit shown in Fig. 11.3 can be used for punched tape control of a pneumatic circuit. If a punched paper tape is fed past the gap sensor, air pulses are produced in the same sequence as the holes punched in the tape.

Pneumatic counting systems are slower to respond than electronic counting systems. A pneumatic counter will count up to 1000 impulses per minute at fairly low pressures. At a pressure of about 5 bars it will only count 600 impulses per minute. An amplifier valve will respond to a maximum of 900 impulses per minute.

The interruptible jet sensor can be used to detect a broken drill on an automatic drilling machine. Drills as small as 1 mm diameter can be detected. The drill interrupts the sensor's air jet (Fig. 11.4). If the drill breaks, a low pressure air signal passes to an amplifier valve. The resulting high pressure air flow sounds an alarm.

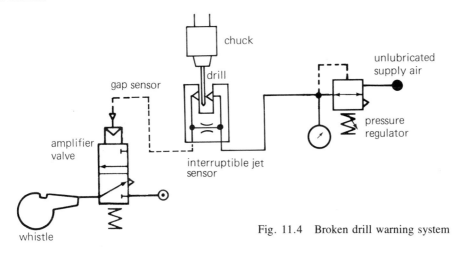

Fig. 11.4   Broken drill warning system

A warning system can be connected to a metalworking lathe to sound an alarm when the carriage approaches the rotating chuck. An emitter is mounted on the bed of the lathe and a rubber pad is attached to the side of the carriage. As the carriage approaches the chuck, the jet from the emitter is occluded. Back pressure builds up above the amplifier valve. High pressure air is released to sound an alarm (Fig. 11.5).

127

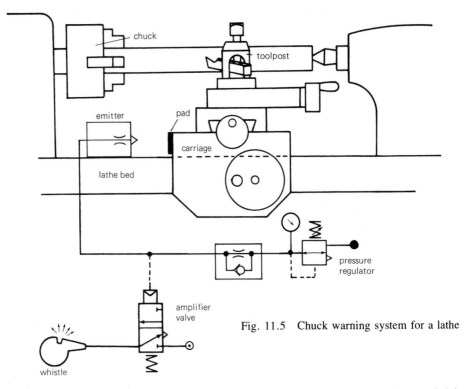

Fig. 11.5 Chuck warning system for a lathe

A method of automatically weighing out identical quantities of bulk material is to use a beam balance (Fig. 11.6). The container to be filled is placed on the beam of a counter-weighted balance. As the container is filled, the beam tilts and interrupts the air jet of a sensor. The high pressure signal from the amplifier valve is removed and the hopper valve closes.

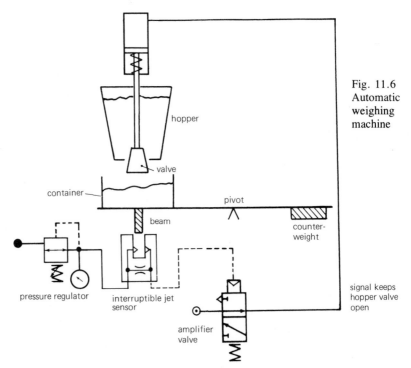

Fig. 11.6
Automatic
weighing
machine

A low pressure circuit can be used as a safety control circuit for a pneumatic punch (Fig. 11.7). The perspex machine guard must be brought down over the punch and die before the machine can be operated. An emitter is connected to an amplifier valve *B* and is supplied with low pressure air from a pressure regulator and a flow regulator. The emitter's jet is occluded when the perspex guard is brought down over the punch. Back pressure builds up and switches the amplifier valve *B*. High pressure air from the amplifier valve *B* is now available to the push-button operated valve *A*. Operation of valve *A* sends an air signal to port 1 2 of the control valve (a double pressure operated 5-port valve). The pneumatic punch operates.

As valves *A* and *B* must be activated to operate the punch, the logic condition for its operation is:

$$A \text{ AND } B = \text{operate}.$$

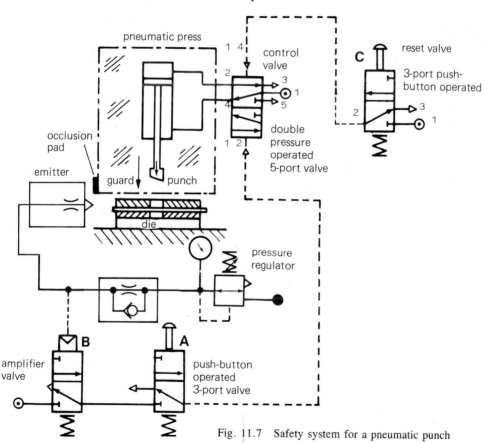

Fig. 11.7 Safety system for a pneumatic punch

Control systems for many machines and processes can be very complex. In order to design such systems a knowledge of logic is required. This is the subject of the remaining sections in this chapter.

◼ Logic

Engineers and designers frequently have to work out control systems for processes and machines. Control requirements can be very complex. However, **logic** can be used to analyse the problem and work out the answer. In 1847, George Boole published a paper entitled 'The Mathematical Analysis of Logic'. Boole's work lay unused for nearly a century, and its worth was only recognised when engineers trying to work out complex control systems used Boole's principles to solve their problems. Boolean Algebra is now seen as an indispensable tool for solving control problems. It enables them to be broken down into small units and expressed in simple terms.

Example 1
Problem: The bell must be capable of being rung from either the front door bell push-button or from the back door bell push-button.
Simple statement: Front button OR Back button $= R$ing bell.
Simpler still: $F + B = R$.

In logic, the $+$ sign means OR.

If there is not a signal from the Front and not a signal from the Back, there is not any Ringing of the bell.
Expressed simply: $\bar{F} \cdot \bar{B} = \bar{R}$.

In logic, the $\cdot$ sign means AND.

In logic, the bar sign ¯ means NOT.

Many control problems can be broken down into a series of simple statements in which OR, AND and NOT are the key words. These simply describe the things which must be true before something can happen – or not happen.

Example 2
Problem: The tank must fill up only when the water is hot and the plug is in place.
Simple statement: Water hot AND Plug in $= F$ill tank.
Simpler still: $W \cdot P = F$
Look now at the three circumstances when the tank will not be filled and try putting each one back into words:

$$\bar{W} \cdot P = \bar{F}$$
$$W \cdot \bar{P} = \bar{F}$$
$$\bar{W} \cdot \bar{P} = \bar{F}$$

In example 2, we could check the water temperature with our hands, use our eyes to check that the plug is in place and our brain to decide if the tank should be filled or not. We could use our hands to turn on the tap. In machines and processes all these things could be required to happen automatically. One sensor will check the water temperature while another checks on the plug. The sensors will communicate with a **decision making device**. This device will only signal the tap to turn on when it is told that the water is hot AND the plug is in.

Fig. 11.8   General logic symbols

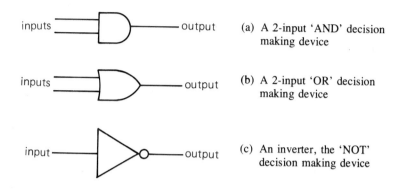

(a) A 2-input 'AND' decision making device

(b) A 2-input 'OR' decision making device

(c) An inverter, the 'NOT' decision making device

Decision making devices can be represented by general symbols. The symbols do not say what the device actually is; they only indicate its function. Figure 11.8a and b shows the general symbols for 'AND' and 'OR' devices. They can have more than two inputs but they always have just one output. The symbols are American in origin and their use is overwhelmingly greater than the use of the British Standard symbols in BS 3939. A careful look-out should be kept for any change in usage and also the requirements of examinations boards.

Another decision making device is the **inverter**, the 'NOT' device (Fig. 11.8c). It has one input and one output. If the input is 'on', the output is 'off' and vice versa. Compare it with the ends of a see-saw!

Example 3

Problem: When the room temperature reaches 20°C the heater must be turned 'off', i.e.

$\overline{20°C} = H$ (NOT 20°C = Heater 'on')

$20°C = \overline{H}$ (20°C = NOT Heater 'on').

At 20°C the temperature sensor turns 'on'. The inverter decides that this has happened. Therefore it turns its output, and hence the heater, 'off'.

Once it has been analysed and worked out, the complete decision making section of a control system can be represented pictorially by joining together the appropriate general symbols. For example, a system requires that if A is 'on' AND B OR C is 'on', then D is turned 'on' AND E is turned 'off'. Put more simply: $A \cdot (B + C) = D \cdot \overline{E}$. This decision making system is shown pictorially in Fig. 11.9.

Fig. 11.9   Decision making system

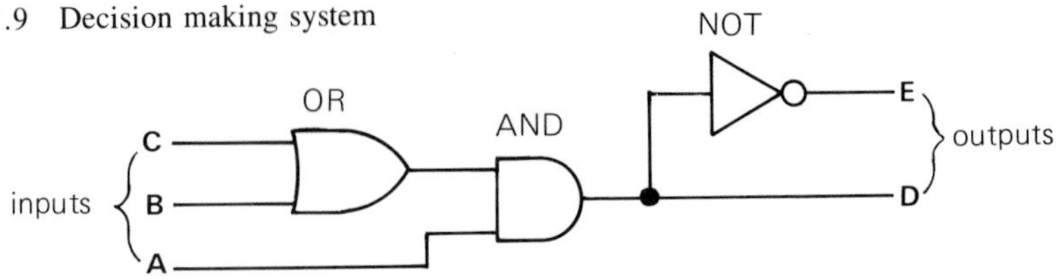

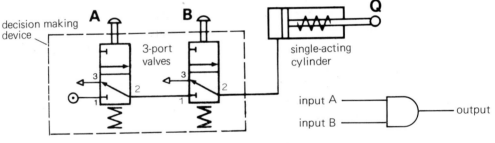

The decision making or **logic device** can be, for example, pneumatic, fluidic, electronic, electrical or mechanical. We shall consider pneumatic and then fluidic logic devices.

☐ Pneumatic Switching Logic

Consider the statement:

The cylinder will outstroke if valve A AND valve B are pressed.

It can be written:

Valve A AND valve B = cylinder outstroke,

that is, $A . B = Q$

(. means AND while Q stands for positive output result).

Using 3-port valves, the circuit shown in Fig. 11.10 will perform according to this statement.

Fig. 11.10   (a) Logic 'AND' circuit $A . B = Q$ (b) Decision making device symbol

When there is no output Q (i.e. NOT Q), this is written $\bar{Q}$. There will be no output Q if an input signal is not present at valve A and valve B at the same time. So,

$$\bar{A} . B = \bar{Q}$$
$$A . \bar{B} = \bar{Q}$$
$$\bar{A} . \bar{B} = \bar{Q}$$

This is one way of describing all possible combinations of input and output for the 'AND' system. However, there is a better way.

Control systems are at their most simple and reliable when each input or output can only be in one of two states, fully 'on' or completely 'off'. The base two, or binary, series of numbers has only two digits, 0 and 1. Binary arithmetic is ideally suited to the task of describing logic control systems fully and concisely. The absence of an input or output signal is indicated by 0. The presence of an input or output signal is indicated by 1. Control systems of this type are often referred to as digital logic systems. Such systems can be very complex as in digital watches, calculators, computers, and now digital recording and broadcasting techniques. The 'works' of all these systems deal with complex patterns of 'ons' and 'offs'. In other words, they process very rapidly long sequences of large binary numbers.

A **truth table** is a compact way of describing all possible combinations of input and output for a logic circuit. Binary digits are used in the truth table. 0 means 'off' and 1 means 'on'. The truth table for the 'AND' circuit shown in Fig. 11.10 is:

Inputs A B	Output Q
0 0	0
0 1	0
1 0	0
1 1	1

Notice that with two inputs there are 2^2 (i.e. 4) possible combinations of input state. The number of inputs in an 'AND' circuit can be increased by increasing the number of 3-port valves connected in series.

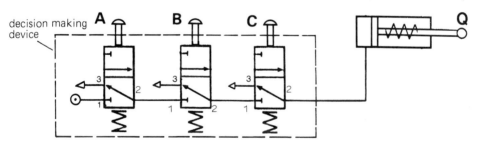

Fig. 11.11   (a) 3-input 'AND' circuit $A \, . \, B \, . \, C = Q$

(b) Decision making device symbol

Valve A AND valve B AND valve C have to be pressed to get an output Q, so
$A \, . \, B \, . \, C = Q$
A circuit with three inputs A, B and C will have 2^3 (i.e. 8) combinations of input.

133

Truth Table for 'AND' Circuit (three inputs)

Inputs			Output
A	B	C	Q
0	0	0	0
0	0	1	0
0	1	0	0
0	1	1	0
1	0	0	0
1	0	1	0
1	1	0	0
1	1	1	1

Another way of connecting two valves together is shown in Fig. 11.12. The output of valve A is fed to the exhaust port of valve B to form an 'OR' circuit.

Fig. 11.12   (a) 'OR' circuit $A + B = Q$

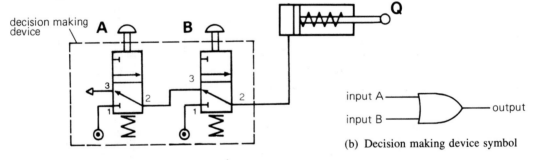

(b) Decision making device symbol

When valve A OR valve B is pressed, the cylinder will go positive and produce an output Q, so

$A + B = Q$ (+ means OR).

The truth table for a 2-input 'OR' circuit is:

'OR' Truth Table

Inputs		Output
A	B	Q
0	0	0
0	1	1
1	0	1
1	1	1

If many valves are connected in this manner to give the 'OR' function, efficient air flow through them becomes difficult. The number of valves should be limited to four. These should be followed by a diaphragm valve, which will restore efficient air flow before the next set of valves (Fig. 11.13*a*). The diaphragm valve acts as a buffer or interface device. When its input is 'on', its output is 'on', and vice versa. Note the general symbol for a buffer in Fig. 11.13*b*.

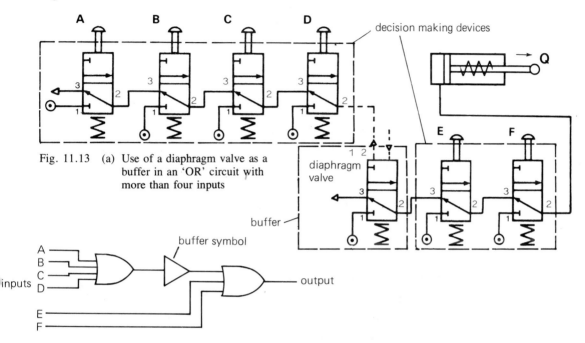

Fig. 11.13 (a) Use of a diaphragm valve as a buffer in an 'OR' circuit with more than four inputs

An alternative method of connecting 'OR' circuits is to use shuttle valves. A shuttle valve has a piston which seals off one inlet port when air is applied at the other inlet port (Fig. 11.14*b*). If a shuttle valve is not used and the 3-port valves connected with a T-connector, then air from one input valve will blow out of the exhaust port of the other valve.

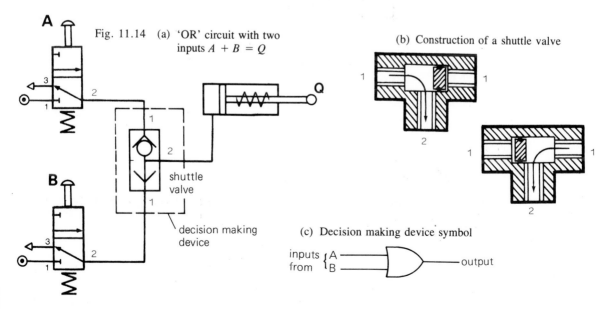

Fig. 11.14 (a) 'OR' circuit with two inputs $A + B = Q$

(b) Construction of a shuttle valve

(c) Decision making device symbol

When valve A OR valve B is pressed, the cylinder will go positive and produce an output Q (Fig. 11.14a), so

valve A OR valve B = output Q.

$$A + B = Q \ (+ \text{ means OR}).$$

The truth table for this 'OR' circuit is:

'OR' Truth Table (two inputs)

Inputs A B	Output Q
0 0	0
0 1	1
1 0	1
1 1	1

When several inputs are required, the shuttle valves are connected in series (Fig. 11.15).

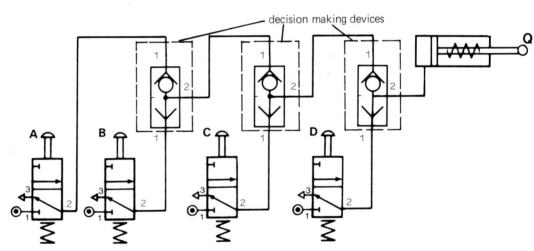

Fig. 11.15   (a) Shuttle valves connected in series for the 'OR' circuit $A + B + C + D = Q$

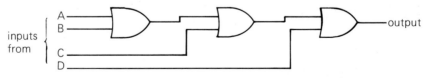

(b) Decision making system symbols

In the 'OR' circuit shown in Fig. 11.15, a signal from valve A OR valve B OR valve C OR valve D will produce an output signal Q, i.e.

$$A + B + C + D = Q \ (+ \text{ means OR}).$$

136

The main disadvantage with shuttle valves connected in series is that the first input signal (from valve A) has to go through all the shuttle valves to produce an output Q. An improved circuit can be achieved with the shuttle valves connected in parallel and series (Fig. 11.16).

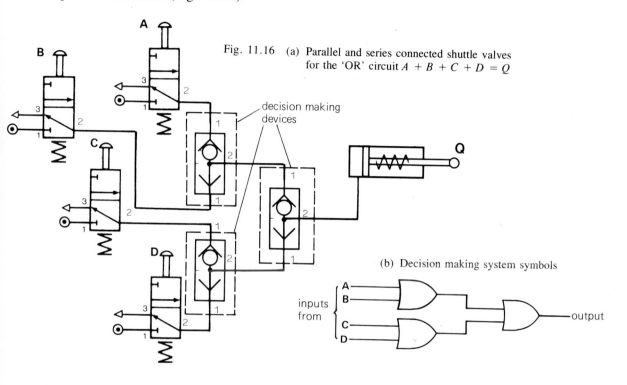

Fig. 11.16 (a) Parallel and series connected shuttle valves for the 'OR' circuit $A + B + C + D = Q$

(b) Decision making system symbols

A signal from valve A OR valve B OR valve C OR valve D will produce an output signal Q, i.e.

$$A + B + C + D = Q.$$

A signal from one of the input valves, say valve A, has to pass through only two shuttle valves before producing an output Q.

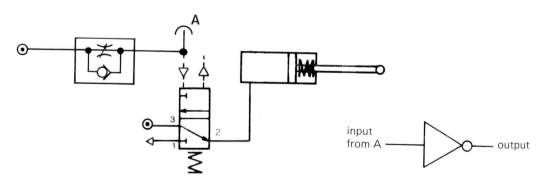

Fig. 11.17 (a) 3-port valve performing the 'NOT' function   (b) Decision making device symbol

The logic function 'NOT' can be performed by a 3-port valve. The air supply is connected to port 3, normally the exhaust port. Port 1 becomes the exhaust port (Fig. 11.17a). Note that this reverse connection can only be done with spool valves and not poppet valves. In the Pneumatics kit, the diaphragm valves are the only spool 3-port valves.

When air jet A is occluded, there is no output Q, i.e.

$$A = \bar{Q} \ (\bar{Q} \text{ means NOT } Q).$$

When air jet A is not occluded, there is an output Q, i.e.

$$\bar{A} = Q \ (\bar{A} \text{ means NOT } A).$$

The truth table for the 'NOT' function is:

Truth Table for 'NOT'

Input A	Output Q
0	1
1	0

☐ The Bistable Unit

Control systems often require bistable units (FLIP-FLOPS). These devices have two (**bi**) outputs, Q and $\bar{Q}$. The outputs remain in (i.e. are **stable** in) whatever 'on' or 'off' state they have been put in by a momentary signal. Because a bistable device remembers a momentary signal it is a **memory device**. The simplest bistable devices have two signal inputs called set (S) and reset (R). A momentary signal at the set input (S) turns the Q output 'on'. The other output is therefore $\bar{Q}$, NOT what output Q is, i.e. it is 'off'. A momentary signal at the reset input (R) turns the Q output 'off'. The other output is therefore $\bar{Q}$, NOT what output Q is, i.e. it is 'on'. This is a different, but important, way of looking at the behaviour of a double pressure operated 5-port valve. This valve is an example of a bistable unit.

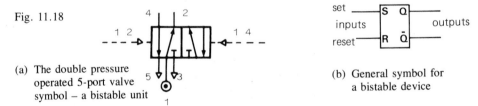

Fig. 11.18

(a) The double pressure operated 5-port valve symbol – a bistable unit

(b) General symbol for a bistable device

Figure 11.18 shows the symbol for the double pressure operated 5-port valve together with the general symbol for a bistable device. With this valve it does not matter which of the signal ports is regarded as set and reset. You will recall that a momentary air signal at signal port 1 2 causes a continuous main air output from port 2 while port 4 is turned 'off'. A momentary air signal at signal port 1 4 causes a continuous main air output from port 4 while port 2 is turned 'off'. The reset signal port is the one which receives a signal which puts a system 'back to the beginning', ready to perform its task. The set signal port is the one which receives a signal which makes a system 'go into action'. An example of the double pressure operated 5-port valve used as a bistable unit is shown in Fig. 11.19. This system selects tall components passing along a conveyor belt. A double-acting cylinder moves a gate which directs the tall components along pathway A. The 5-port valve is used to control the cylinder. It is set and reset by two low pressure jet detection circuits.

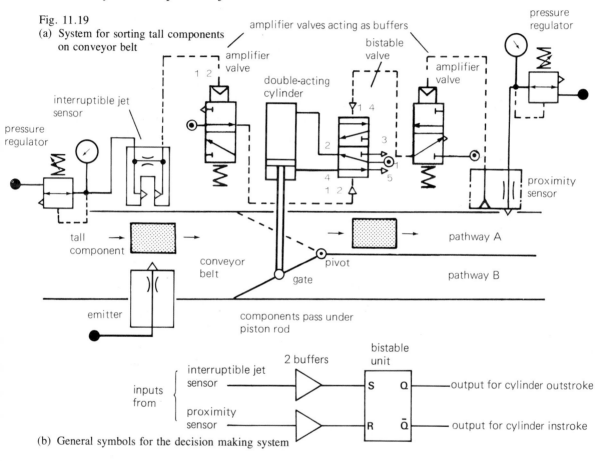

Fig. 11.19
(a) System for sorting tall components on conveyor belt

(b) General symbols for the decision making system

Tall components approaching the gate are detected by a long distance gap sensing system. When the emitter's air jet is broken by a tall component, a low pressure output signal is produced by the interruptible jet sensor. This signal operates the amplifier valve buffer. A high pressure signal from the amplifier valve sets the bistable (5-port valve). The double-acting cylinder goes positive, allowing tall components to move down pathway A.

A tall component passing the proximity sensor in pathway A resets the bistable. The cylinder then goes negative and small components are directed along pathway B.

□ An Example of Pneumatic Logic

A control system for a power press is required. The press should only be oper-
able if the guard is down and a two-button safety control is pressed. It must be
possible to reset the press from either one of two remote push-button valves.

Assume that the down position of the guard is sensed by a roller-trip valve
(Fig. 11.20). The safety control valves are push-button operated valves B and
C. The reset valves in remote positions are valves D or E.
The operating condition now reads:

To operate the pneumatic power press, valve A AND valve B AND valve C
must be activated.

This can be presented as the logic statement: $A.B.C = Set$
The reset condition now reads:

To reset the power press, valve D OR valve E must be activated.

This can be presented as the logic statement: $D + E = Reset$
The 'AND' condition is achieved by connecting the input valves A, B and C in
series. The 'OR' reset condition is achieved by connecting the valves D and E to
a shuttle valve. The final circuit is shown in Fig. 11.20.

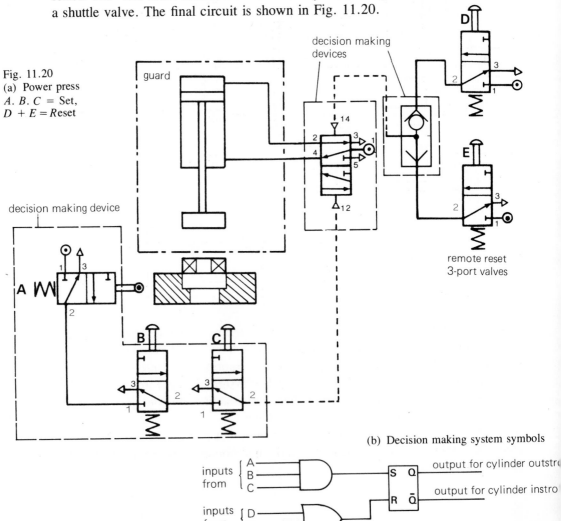

Fig. 11.20
(a) Power press
$A.B.C = Set,$
$D + E = Reset$

decision making
devices

guard

decision making device

remote reset
3-port valves

(b) Decision making system symbols

inputs from { A B C

inputs from { D E

output for cylinder outstr
output for cylinder instro

☐ Fluid Logic (Fluidic) Devices

In Chapter 10 the turbulence amplifier principle was introduced. A turbulence amplifier is a small device which can be used to perform logic functions. It is a fluid logic (fluidic) device with no moving parts. A 2-input turbulence amplifier which performs the 'NOT OR' (NOR) logic function was described. All other logic functions can be obtained by interconnecting 'NOR' devices in the appropriate way.

Another fluidic device with no moving parts and which can perform logic functions is the **wall attachment device**. Turbulence amplifiers can only perform the 'NOT' and 'NOR' functions, and their speed of operation is low. With wall attachment devices, a range of logic functions is available in the form of small modular devices whose speed of operation is high.

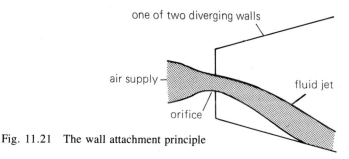

Fig. 11.21   The wall attachment principle

Figure 11.21 shows a jet of fluid issuing from an orifice. The orifice is placed symmetrically between two diverging walls. The fluid jet does not travel in a straight line between the two walls. Instead, it always bends and attaches itself to one or other of the two walls. This is known as the **Coanda effect** after Henri Coanda who discovered it in 1932. Which of the two walls the fluid jet attaches to is a matter of chance.

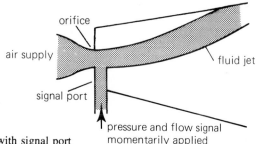

Fig. 11.22   Wall attachment device with signal port

Figure 11.22 shows a symmetrical wall attachment device fitted with a signal port. A momentary air signal applied at the signal port makes the fluid jet detach itself from the lower wall and attach itself to the upper wall. The jet stays attached to the upper wall even when the signal is removed. To return the fluid jet to the lower wall, a port must be fitted in the upper wall through which another momentary signal can be given (Fig. 11.23).

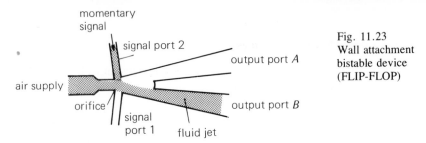

Fig. 11.23
Wall attachment
bistable device
(FLIP-FLOP)

Figure 11.23 shows a wall attachment device with two signal ports and two separate exits (output port A and output port B) for the fluid jet. A momentary signal at port 1 makes the jet move to output A. A momentary signal at port 2 makes the jet return to output B. This is a bistable device (a FLIP-FLOP) and it performs a switching function identical to that of a double pressure operated 5-port valve. If each output is connected to an amplifier valve, the bistable wall attachment device can be used to control a high pressure pneumatic circuit. The amplifier valve is an interface device, or buffer.

Fig. 11.24   Assymetrical wall
              attachment device

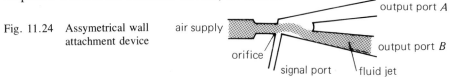

Figure 11.24 shows an assymetrical wall attachment device. The orifice is nearer one attachment wall than the other. The fluid jet leaving the orifice always attaches itself to the nearer wall. The fluid jet leaves the device by output port B.

If a signal is applied and maintained at the signal port (Fig. 11.25), the fluid jet attaches itself to the opposite wall and now leaves by output port A. If the signal is removed, output A turns 'off' again. Used in this way, the wall attachment device's behaviour is comparable with that of an air-operated, spring-returned 3-port valve, e.g. a diaphragm valve, which turns 'on' and stays 'on' as long as an air signal is applied.

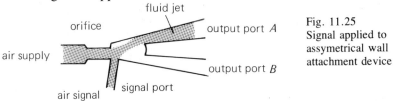

Fig. 11.25
Signal applied to
assymetrical wall
attachment device

Amplifier valves can be connected to output port A or B or both. An amplifier valve connected to port B is 'on' when there is *no* signal at the signal port (Fig. 11.24). This amplifier valve is NOT 'on' when there *is* a signal at the signal port (Fig. 11.25). Used in this way, the wall attachment device is behaving as an **inverter** and is performing the logic 'NOT' function. An amplifier valve connected to port A is not 'on' when there is no signal at the signal port (Fig. 11.24). This amplifier valve is 'on' when there is a signal at the signal port (Fig. 11.25).

Signal ports can be arranged in different ways to give different logic functions. Figure 11.26 shows the 'OR-NOR' arrangement. An air signal at port 2 OR 3 OR 4 (OR any combination of them) causes an output from output port A. This is the 'OR' function. The opposite function, 'NOR' (NOT OR), is also available. When there is a signal at port 2 OR 3 OR 4 (OR any combination of them), there is NOT an output from output port B. Which of the outputs, A or B, is used depends on the application being dealt with. Figure 11.26 shows the wall attachment device fitted with vents in addition to its other openings. Vents similar to these are found in all wall attachment logic devices. They are required to spill excess air to atmosphere.

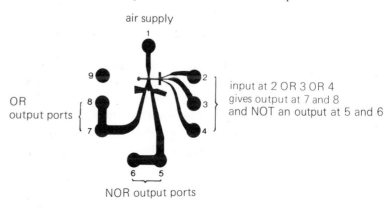

Fig. 11.26   An OR-NOR signal ported assymetrical wall attachment device

An OR-NOR module is included in the equipment kit (Fig. 11.27a). It has three signal input ports (ports 2, 3 and 4), two 'OR' output ports (ports 7 and 8), and two 'NOR' output ports (ports 5 and 6). The supply to the fluid jet is through port 1. Figure 11.27b shows the layout of the airways within the OR-NOR module and identifies the ports. The air supply pressure to port 1 should be between 0.5 and 1 bar. Very low air pressure signals are sufficient to control the device. A signal of 12% of the supply pressure will activate the device. It deactivates when the signal pressure falls below 1% of the supply pressure.

Fig. 11.27   (a) The OR-NOR module

(b) The airways in the OR-NOR module and port identification

Input signals to the OR-NOR module can be given by the proximity sensor, the touch sensor or the interruptible jet sensor. Each output port can drive one device only, e.g. an amplifier valve, or signal another fluidic module. The tube from an output port should not be branched. Where only one of a pair of output ports is being used, the other unused port should be blanked off with the small cap supplied with the module. Where a set of output ports is unused they can be left to vent to atmosphere.

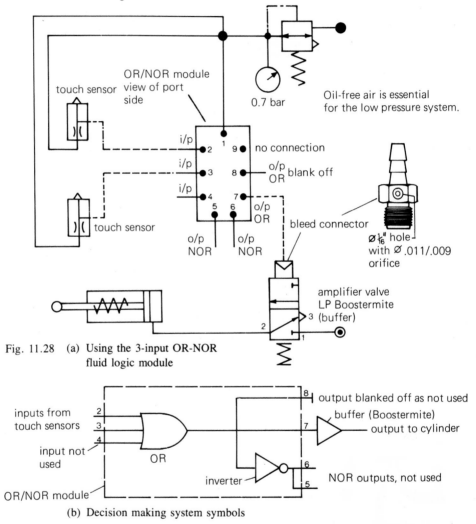

Fig. 11.28   (a)   Using the 3-input OR-NOR fluid logic module

(b) Decision making system symbols

Figure 11.28 shows a circuit using the OR-NOR module. Only two inputs are being used and signals are obtained from touch sensors. The cylinder will out-stroke when the air bleed from one OR other (OR both) touch sensor is occluded. The amplifier valve is 'on' when an air pressure signal is applied to its signal port. The amplifier valve can only turn 'off' again when air pressure in its signal line decays. This pressure decay can only happen if there is an air flow back along the signal line and out to atmosphere through a vent in the logic module. This takes time and can delay the amplifier's 'off' response. To overcome this, the amplifier valve's signal port is fitted with a bleed connector. This allows signal air pressure to decay rapidly by allowing a flow of air to atmosphere through the connector's bleed hole (Fig. 11.28). The bleed connector is dyed red to distinguish it from ordinary barbed connectors.

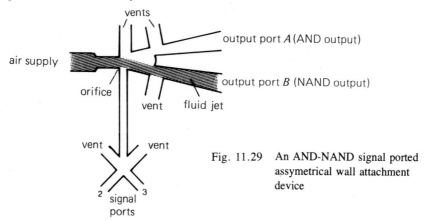

Fig. 11.29   An AND-NAND signal ported assymetrical wall attachment device

A range of logic modules is manufactured by IMI Norgren Ltd. As well as OR-NOR, it includes AND-NAND (Fig. 11.29) and FLIP-FLOP. This latter is a bistable, or memory module. Figure 11.30 shows the airways and port identification of the AND-NAND and FLIP-FLOP modules. When funds permit, your school may be able to purchase these and other modules to extend the range of practical work in this course, and to extend the control system possibilities in project work. With these modules it is possible to quickly learn about control functions that are often performed by electronic integrated circuits (silicon chips) or computers.

Fig. 11.30

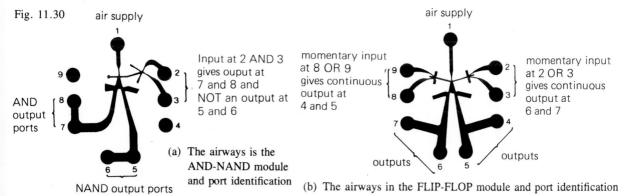

Input at 2 AND 3 gives ouput at 7 and 8 and NOT an output at 5 and 6

(a) The airways is the AND-NAND module and port identification

momentary input at 8 OR 9 gives continuous output at 4 and 5

momentary input at 2 OR 3 gives continuous output at 6 and 7

(b) The airways in the FLIP-FLOP module and port identification

Answers to Questions

1 Read the number of pulses registered by the pneumatic counter in one minute and divide the number by two.

2 By the use of different counter-weights.

12 Mini Projects

■ Introduction

One of the options in this pneumatics course is to tackle a mini project. A **project** is an activity in which you plan, organise and carry out your own study and practical work. Project activity is centred on a topic or theme. It can be undertaken individually or in groups.

Technology projects can be divided into two kinds: constructional projects and investigational projects. The investigational project is a 'study' project. Both kinds involve analysis of a problem, enquiry, alternative solutions, selection and decision making and the development of a solution. Investigational projects conclude with the writing of a substantial report. Constructional projects conclude with the design, production, testing and evaluation of hardware. Technology projects are essentially creative. Ideally, they are undertaken for humanitarian reasons in order to meet the needs of people.

A mini project is an exercise in problem solving designed to take from two to four weeks. In such a short time the production of working hardware is unlikely. All the same, the exercise of a mini project gives valuable experience for later work in technology.

■ Projects

Any project should be tackled in several clearly defined stages. These stages are summarised in Fig. 12.1.

The Need

Make a clear statement of the human need which, because it is not met, creates a problem.

Brief and Specification

Give concise details of the nature of the problem. In the specification, include any design constraints, e.g. the time available, the materials and equipment available, the environment in which project hardware has to work, any social and environmental considerations. Keep the brief and specification precise.

Analysis and Investigation

Assess what the problem involves. Break down the major problem into smaller subsidiary problems. Make a block diagram of the subsidiary problems and then consider, in outline, possible solutions. Gather together any data or circuit information required. Circuit ideas can be obtained from this and other books in the series.

Alternative Solutions

Suggest at least three alternative solutions, including those developed from other areas of technology. Discuss solutions and communicate ideas in a visual form. Use sketches, circuit diagrams, block diagrams and graphs. Notes can be added to the illustrative material.

Selection of a Solution

Decide which of the alternative solutions will be developed into hardware. The solution must be capable of construction in the time available. Structures to hold components can be produced easily if construction kit materials such as Meccano, Hybridex, Dexion or Handy Angle are used.

Give reasons for the solution decision made. Give reasons why the other solutions were rejected.

Realisation

Obtain the components required for the chosen solution. Some fixings, small parts and base structures may have to be made. The manufacture of hardware takes a large amount of project time.

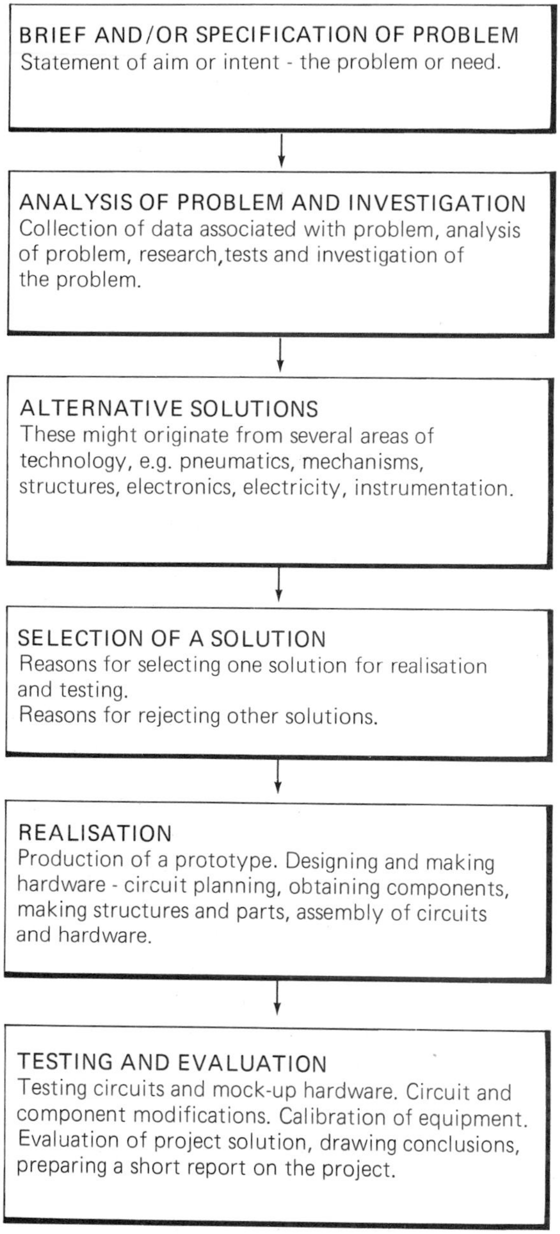

Testing and Evaluation

Test the solution when it is built. It may be necessary to make modifications. Re-test the solution.

Write a critical evaluation of the solution in a report. Make suggestions for modifications. If the project was not completely successful, analyse why and suggest ways of overcoming the problems.

BRIEF AND/OR SPECIFICATION OF PROBLEM
Statement of aim or intent - the problem or need.

↓

ANALYSIS OF PROBLEM AND INVESTIGATION
Collection of data associated with problem, analysis of problem, research, tests and investigation of the problem.

↓

ALTERNATIVE SOLUTIONS
These might originate from several areas of technology, e.g. pneumatics, mechanisms, structures, electronics, electricity, instrumentation.

↓

SELECTION OF A SOLUTION
Reasons for selecting one solution for realisation and testing.
Reasons for rejecting other solutions.

↓

REALISATION
Production of a prototype. Designing and making hardware - circuit planning, obtaining components, making structures and parts, assembly of circuits and hardware.

↓

TESTING AND EVALUATION
Testing circuits and mock-up hardware. Circuit and component modifications. Calibration of equipment. Evaluation of project solution, drawing conclusions, preparing a short report on the project.

Fig. 12.1   Stages of a constructional project

147

■ A Mini Project Timetable

Try to plan how the time available will be spent in different stages of the mini project. If four weeks are available for the mini project, including homework time, a possible time plan for two or three pupils working as a group could be as follows.

Week 1 Write brief and specification. Analyse the problem, collect data such as circuit ideas. Begin writing and drawing alternative solution ideas. Discuss ideas in the group.

Homework Write and draw up alternative solutions in notebook (aim at three alternative solutions). Only ideas, small sketches, notes and circuits are required.

Week 2 Select a solution to develop. Give reasons for its selection. Collect components required and materials for parts. Pipe up circuit. Test, if this is possible.

Homework Make detailed drawing of chosen solution circuit. List components required.

Week 3 Manufacture fixing parts for components. Delegate work in the group.

Homework Sketch any manufactured parts, give dimensions, materials, joining techniques.

Week 4 Assemble mock-up hardware and circuit. Test the hardware. Make minor modifications.

Homework Write up evaluation in notebook.

Experience shows that manufacture of hardware takes a considerable time. The mini project may be confined to an exercise on paper, together with the bench testing of a suitable pneumatic circuit. Each problem given in Activity 12 is capable of being a major project, requiring the production of well engineered hardware.

■ An Example of Problem Solving – A Fabric Tester

The Need

There is a need for a means of testing and comparing the wear properties of various fabrics.

Design Brief and Specification

Design and make a machine to test the wear properties of fabric samples. A machine is required which will accurately record the abrasion needed to wear through each sample of material. A quantitative comparison of the fabric wear properties is essential. The fabric tester must be constructed in a school workshop. The samples of fabric available are approximately 250 mm × 150 mm. Compressed air and electrical power supplies are available.

Analysis and Investigation of Problem

The problem can be divided into subsidiary problems.

1 Designing a method for holding the fabric sample.
2 Choosing an abrasive surface to rub or wear the fabric.
3 Designing means of causing movement between the abrasive surface and the fabric sample.
4 Designing a method of measuring the amount of abrasion.
5 Recording or displaying this measurement.

This analysis of the problem can be summarised by a block diagram (Fig. 12.2).

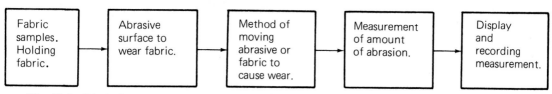

Fig. 12.2   Block diagram of design problem

An outline solution of each subsidiary problem is indicated in the block diagram shown in Fig. 12.3. Note that the energy converting devices will require their own power sources.

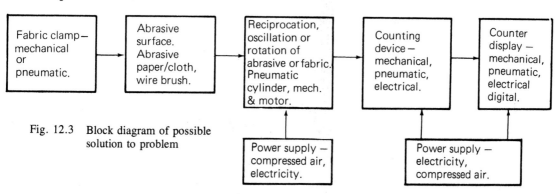

Fig. 12.3   Block diagram of possible solution to problem

Since the problem of designing a fabric tester has been divided into five parts, it is useful to consider and list devices that could be used to solve each subsidiary problem.

1 *Fabric Clamp*
   (a) Mechanical: screw clamp, wedges, toggle clamps, levers or linkages, weights, cams, springs.
   (b) Pneumatic: single-acting cylinder to clamp or stretch fabric.
   (c) Electrical: solenoid clamping, electromagnetic clamping device.

2 *Abrasive Surface*
   Glasspaper, emery cloth, silicon carbide paper, wire brush, file card, bristle brush, carborundum stone, grooved surface such as metalwork file or Surform blade.

149

3 *Method of Movement (Reciprocating, Oscillating or Rotary)*
   (a) Pneumatic: double-acting cylinder; different types of valve control.
   (b) Electro-mechanical: crank and slider mechanism with electric motor, rack and pinion with electric motor, cam and follower with electric motor, solenoid and spring return; electric motor.

4 *Counting Device*
   (a) Pneumatic/fluidic: gap sensor, air stream detector, proximity sensor, touch or lever sensor (requires amplifier valve).
   (b) Electrical: reed switch and magnet, microswitch.
   (c) Electronic: photocell or light-dependent resistor, phototransistor.
   (d) Mechanical: lever or toggle counter.

5 *Counter Display*
   (a) Mechanical: lever or toggle counter (like the ones used on bicycles to record distance).
   (b) Electrical: electromagnetic counter (digital).
   (c) Electronic: digital displays.
   (d) Pneumatic: pneumatic counter.

Circuit ideas to solve the problem can be found in the
   Pneumatics module, Chapter 7, Automatic Circuits;
   Mechanisms module, Chapter 6, Crank/Slider Mechanisms;
   Electronics module, Chapter 4, Interface Devices.

Alternative Solutions
Figure 12.4 shows several alternative methods of securing the fabric samples.

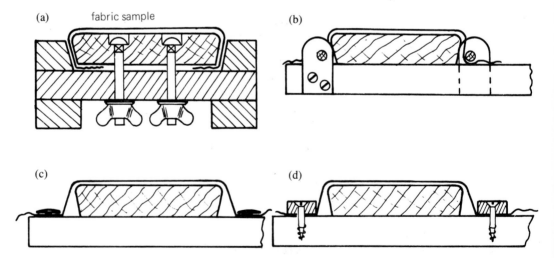

Fig. 12.4 Design ideas for securing fabric samples

The abrasive medium can be a wire brush or glasspaper block. Figure 12.5 shows a mechanical method of moving a wire brush across the fabric sample. A crank/slider mechanism will produce reciprocating motion. The mechanism could be driven by an electric motor.

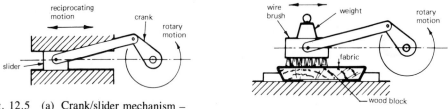

Fig. 12.5   (a) Crank/slider mechanism –
reciprocating motion

(b) Fabric testing machine

A pneumatic double-acting cylinder can be used to provide reciprocating motion. Five different pneumatic circuits are shown in Figs. 12.6 to 12.10.

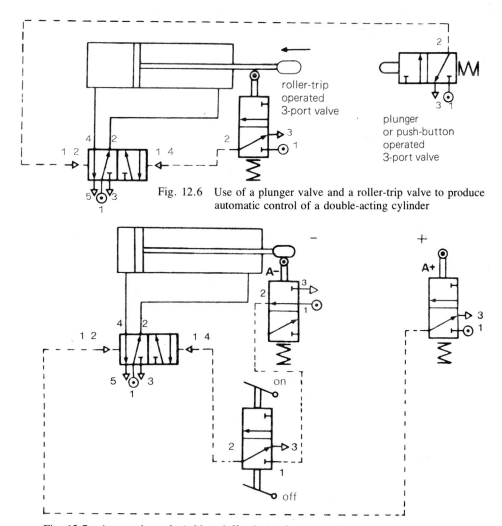

Fig. 12.6   Use of a plunger valve and a roller-trip valve to produce automatic control of a double-acting cylinder

Fig. 12.7   Automatic cycle (with on/off valve) using two roller-trip pilot valves

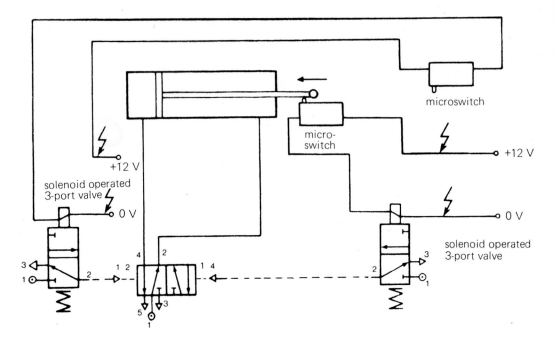

Fig. 12.8   Solenoid valves and microswitches used to produce automatic control circuit

Fig. 12.9   Automatic control circuit using time delay

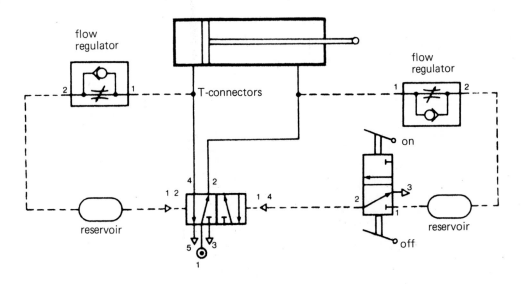

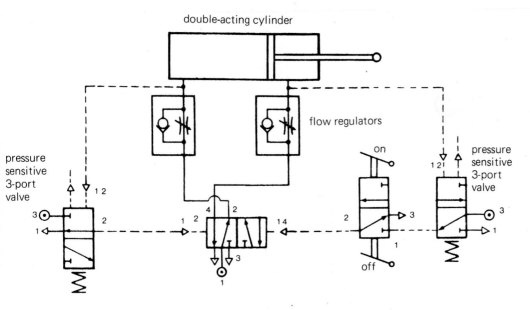

Fig. 12.10   Using pressure sensitive valves to produce automatic control

A simple electrical counting circuit with display is shown in Fig. 12.11. An electromagnetic counter is used to register the number of brush strokes. The count is produced by the opening and closing of a microswitch.

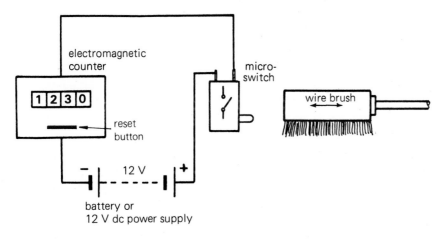

Fig. 12.11   Electrical counting circuit

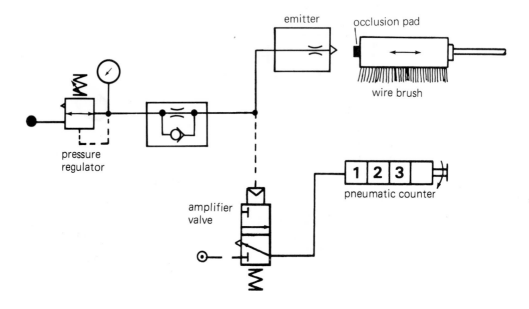

Fig. 12.12   Air-operated counting circuit

An air-operated circuit for counting is shown in Fig. 12.12. An air jet is used to detect the strokes of the wire brush. Low pressure air is supplied by a pressure regulator and flow regulator. An amplifier valve is used to send high pressure air signals to a pneumatic counter.

Selection of a Solution

The solution chosen for development is shown in Fig. 12.13. The fabric is clamped by wooden wedge-shaped blocks and screw bolts. This is cheap, easy to construct and provides a very secure method of fixing the fabric without causing damage to it.

A pneumatic circuit is used to reciprocate the wire brush chosen to wear the fabric. The pneumatic circuit uses reservoirs and flow regulators to produce automatic reciprocation. This circuit has the advantage of not requiring mechanical or electrical trip valves.

An air operated counting system is used as this saves having two different power sources. A microswitch and electromagnetic counter would need a 12 V dc power supply.

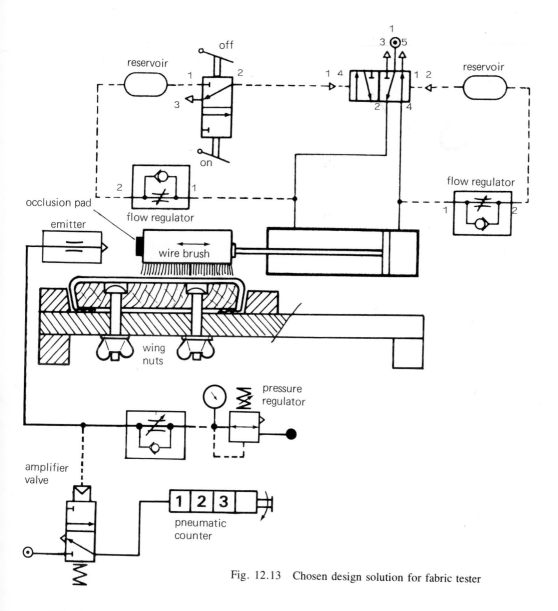

Fig. 12.13   Chosen design solution for fabric tester

TEST RESULTS

Fabric Sample	No. of Strokes to Wear through Sample
A Wool 100%	220
B Wool/nylon mixture	250
C Cotton 100%	180
D Polyester	240
E Terylene	280

The conclusion drawn from the fabric tests is that man-made fabrics are more wear-resistant than natural fibre fabrics.

The pneumatic fabric tester and the fluidic/pneumatic stroke counter worked well. However,

1 the point at which a fabric is considered to have worn through is difficult to judge;
2 the pressure on the fabric is not adjustable;
3 an electrical counting circuit would prove cheaper on component costs although it requires a separate dc power supply.

Future developments could:

1 allow fabric testing with a range of weights on the wire brush to vary wear pressure;
2 investigate different abrasive surfaces for wearing the fabric.